This b

L(

MW00844283

Author and Editor: M.Eng. Johannes Wild
A94689H39927F
Email: 3dtech@gmx.de

The complete imprint of the book can be found on the last pages!

This work is protected by copyright

The work, including its parts, is protected by copyright. Any use outside the narrow limits of copyright law without the consent of the author is prohibited. This applies in particular to electronic or other reproduction, translation, distribution and making publicly available. No part of the work may be reproduced, processed or distributed without written permission of the author! All rights reserved.

All information contained in this book has been compiled to the best of our knowledge and has been carefully checked. However, the publisher and the author do not guarantee the timeliness, accuracy, completeness, and quality of the information provided. This book is for educational purposes only and does <u>not</u> constitute a recommendation for action. The use of this book and the implementation of the information contained therein is expressly at your own risk. In particular, no warranty or liability is given for damages of a material or immaterial nature on the part of the author and publisher for the use or non-use of information in this book. This book does not claim to be complete or error-free. Legal claims and claims for damages are excluded. The operators of the respective Internet sites referred to in this book are exclusively responsible for the content of their site. The publisher and the author have no influence on the design and contents of third-party internet websites. The publisher and author therefore distance themselves from all external content. At the time of use, no illegal content was present on the websites. The trademarks and common names cited in this book remain the sole property of the respective author or right's holder.

Thank you so much for choosing this book!

Table of Contents

Legal information 1

Table of Contents 2

Foreword.. 4

1 Introduction to CAD and "FreeCAD" **5**

1.1 What is CAD and what is "FreeCAD"?..5

1.2 Basic information on CAD design 7

1.3 Download procedure...9

1.4 Installation procedure 10

2 First steps with "FreeCad"... **13**

2.1 "FreeCad" Basic settings...13

2.2 "FreeCAD" Program environment 17

2.2.1 Home page 17
2.2.2 Workspace...17

3 The basic workspaces in "FreeCAD" **21**

3.1 General information 21

3.2 The "Part Design" Workspace - Part 1: General Information 22

3.3 The "Sketcher" Workspace: Creating a 2D sketch...31

3.3.1 General and important settings 31
3.3.2 Geometric elements for creating a 2D sketch...34
3.3.3 Modifying a 2D sketch 39
3.3.4 The constraints..42
3.4 The "Part Design" Workspace - Part 2: 3D Modeling 57

3.4.1 Additive tools 57
3.4.2 Subtractive tools..70
3.4.3 Tools for mirroring and pattern creation 85
3.4.4 Tools for advanced 3D modeling..89

4 Design projects **93**

4.1 First project: mounting component 93

4.2 Second project: Hexagon socket bolt 100

4.3 Third project: mug with handle 110

4.4 Fourth project: Screwdriver 119

5 Other Workspaces in "FreeCAD" **126**

5.1 The "Assembly (A2 Plus)" Workspace 126

5.1.1 The constraint "centerOfMass" 140

5.1.2 The constraint "pointIdentity" 141

5.1.3 The constraint "circularEdge" 142

5.1.4 The constraint "pointOnLine" 143

5.1.5 The constraint "angledPlanes" 144

5.2 The "TechDraw" Workspace...145

6 Conclusion **157**

Imprint of the author / publisher... **161**

Foreword

Thank you very much for selecting this book!

Are you interested in designing three-dimensional objects using "FreeCAD"?

Then, this is the ultimate book for you! I am an engineer and would like to teach you the design of 3D objects in a simple and easy to understand way. For this purpose, we use the semi-professional CAD software "FreeCAD", which you can download for FREE! In this course, you will learn everything you need to know to create three-dimensional components, to assemble them virtually and to derive technical drawings from them.

Here is the link to download the software:

https://www.freecadweb.org

We will take a detailed look at how the installation process works in a moment.

This comprehensive and detailed course is specifically designed for beginners and shows you from scratch how to use the software and how CAD designs succeed. You don't need any previous knowledge for this book, as everything is explained to you step by step and in detail. In addition to many theoretical explanations on how to use the software, you will also learn by means of some great design projects!

So, in this course, you will learn everything you need to know as a beginner! Start into the fascinating world of CAD design with "FreeCAD"! Let's go!

1 Introduction to CAD and "FreeCAD"

1.1 What is CAD and what is "FreeCAD"?

Hello and welcome to the "FreeCAD" course for beginners!

Thank you for choosing this course!

What is CAD?

As you may already know, the abbreviation CAD stands for "Computer-Aided Design". CAD software is used to create or edit three-dimensional objects. Starting with simple individual parts, through complex parts, to entire assemblies that can be virtually assembled. In this course, specifically designed for beginners, you will learn how the environment of a CAD program is structured and how to make the best use of each feature to create three-dimensional objects. You will be able to recreate each design project step-by-step and one-to-one, to get an easy start in design and to become more familiar with the multiple functions of a CAD program with each project.

In brief, this course allows you to learn the following in detail:

- To be able to use the program environment of "FreeCAD" quickly and safely,
- Safely master all major functions,
- Understand the basics of CAD design and the different ways of working,
- The 2D sketches and 3D object creation,
- Create individual parts and assemblies,
- Virtually assemble individual parts into assemblies,
- Create technical drawings in "FreeCAD".

It is best to stay in the order that the course provides, as the lessons build on each other. If you do not understand the individual chapters, functions, or commands right away or miss the explanation for a function, just stay tuned. The course is structured so that all important and basic functions are sufficiently explained.

What is "FreeCAD"?

"FreeCAD" is an open-source 3D CAD software, which is specifically intended for mechanical engineering and product design, but can also be used in the field of architecture or other technical areas. This program offers a clear and simple user interface and is also available for **free**! The structure of the design features is very similar to the professional and very expensive CAD programs that you use as an engineer or technician in everyday work. Professional CAD program licenses like "SolidWorks", "Catia", "SolidEdge" or "AutoCAD" and "Inventor" cost however one to several thousand dollars and are worthwhile themselves therefore usually only for professional users and self-employed persons.

"FreeCAD" was developed for designing real things using 3D parametric modeling. In parametric modeling, one constructs objects with the help of parameters. This means that to construct a rectangular 3D body, for example, you need the three parameters length, width, and height and build the body using these three dimensions. The previously mentioned professional CAD programs (e.g., "SolidWorks" or "Autodesk Inventor") also use this type of modeling.

The advantage of this is that the individual parameters can be varied at any time, making it easy to make adjustments or changes to the geometry of the body even after the 3D object has been completed.

All common CAD programs work in a very identical way, which we will briefly look at below.

1.2 Basic information on CAD design

In CAD design, a distinction is made between a two-dimensional and a three-dimensional area. In the two-dimensional area, 2D sketches are created, which can then be transformed into 3D objects with the help of commands.

Thus, to create a 3D model, a 2D sketch of the desired object must first be made. This is done with simple geometric elements, such as: Line, circle, rectangle, and polygon. You can imagine the creation of a 2D sketch as drawing in the program "Microsoft Paint". This 2D sketch is made on a plane of the three-dimensional space and then transformed into a three-dimensional object with the help of a command (e.g., extrusion command).

Imagine, for example, that you are looking at the top of a simple three-dimensional object. In the case of a cylinder, for example, what do you see when you look at it from above, at a perfect right angle to the top surface of the body? Correct, a two-dimensional circle, nothing else. And it is exactly from this 2D shape that the 3D cylinder is created in the CAD program. It is exactly this circle geometry that we have to draw in the first step. The three-dimensional shape is then obtained through further command steps.

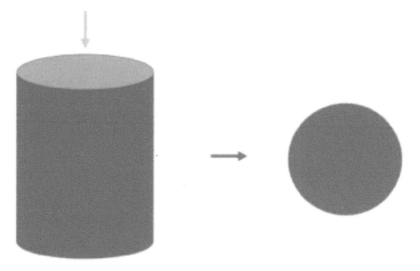

And this approach applies not only to a cylinder, but also to many other 3D objects. For example, you can create a cuboid by drawing a rectangle in a sketch on a 2D plane of space. And with the help of dimensions, you can define the shape of the object. For the two-dimensional rectangle you need a length "a" and a width "b" and for the final 3D object you also need a height "h". For the cylinder, on the other hand, you would define a diameter or a radius for the circular surface, as well as a height for the cylinder. Two dimensions would be sufficient here.

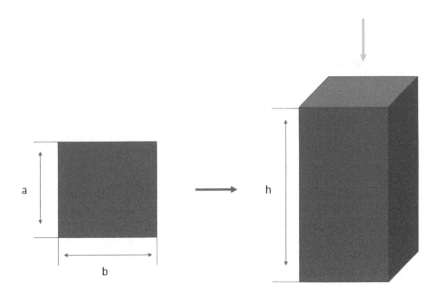

How to design such simple - and later more complicated - 3D objects with "FreeCAD", you can learn in detail and step by step in the further course.

By the way, there are various methods for approaching the individual constructions, which vary greatly depending on the designer and the 3D object, but which can all ultimately lead to the goal. So, there is not only one way, and you are welcome to think along which other way, the individual objects could still be constructed. Sometimes a different approach leads easier or faster to the goal, sometimes the opposite is also the case.

Another tip for using the course: The best and most effective way to learn how to use the CAD software is to first look carefully at the individual design steps, then put the book aside briefly after 3-4 steps, and then try to copy the steps shown on your own without further help. It is best to use this approach throughout the entire course of this book.

In the next sections, you will first learn more about the installation and the program interface of the software "FreeCAD". After we have made a few general settings, we will then deal in detail with the creation of a 2D sketch, as well as the subsequent transfer of the sketch into a 3D object.

Let's start with the installation of the program!

1.3 Download procedure

"FreeCAD" can be downloaded for free. The procedure is very simple and is described step by step below:

Step 1: Open your Internet browser and go to the official website https://www.freecadweb.org or search for the term "FreeCAD" in a search engine of your choice.

Step 2: Click on the "Download now" option.

Step 3: On the next page, you need to select the desired platform, e.g., Windows 64-bit. After clicking the corresponding button, the download will start automatically.

1.4 Installation procedure

The following describes the installation process for a Windows PC.

Step 1: Right-click on the downloaded setup file and run it as administrator: "Run as administrator".

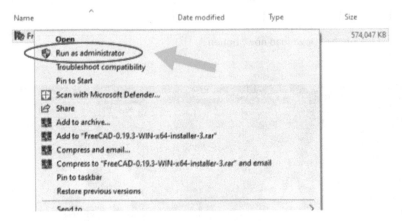

Step 2: Follow the instructions of the software for installation.

Step 3: When selecting users, consider whether only you should use the program or other user accounts on your PC should also have access to it. If you are not sure what this means, you can simply select the option "Install for anyone using this computer".

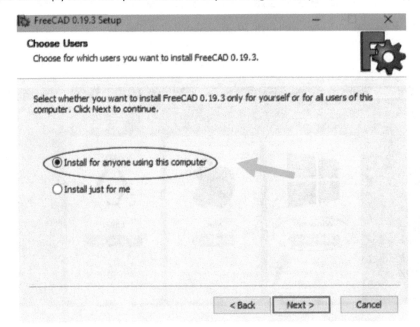

Step 4: Then follow the rest of the installation process and check all the boxes when selecting the components to install.

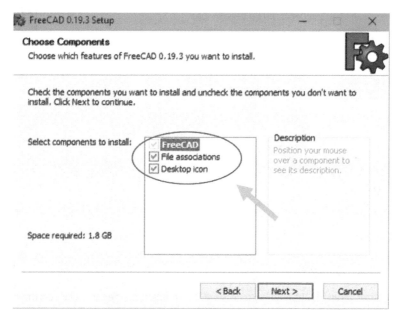

Step 5: When selecting the Start Menu folder, you can simply leave the default settings and click the "Install" button to install the program.

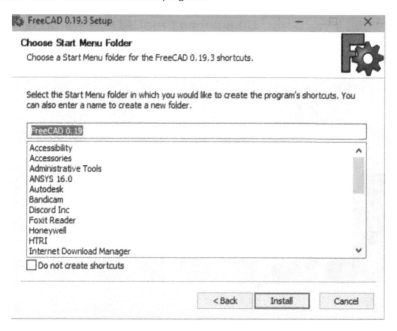

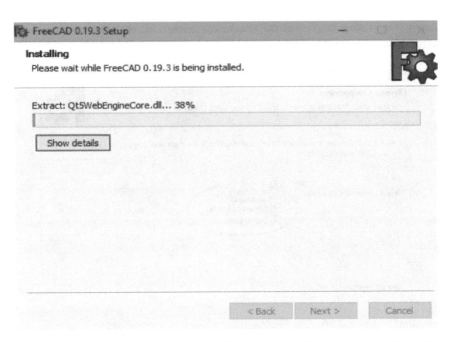

Step 6: After a few minutes, the process will be completed. Then just click on the button "Finish".

2 First steps with "FreeCad"

After we have installed the program, we can start it for the first time. The start page should then look like this:

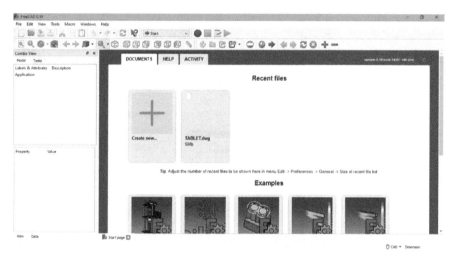

2.1 "FreeCad" Basic settings

Before we can start with the CAD design, we will first briefly deal with the settings of the program. To do this, click on the button "Edit" and select the option "Preferences ...".

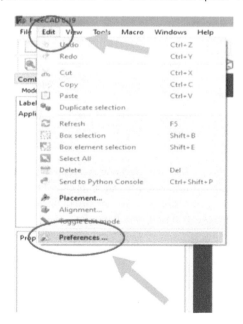

The program "FreeCAD" automatically selects the language of your operating system when you start it for the first time. However, you can also change this setting in the "General" section. We set the program language to English.

A little further down, in the section "Main window", you can change the color of the display. However, if this is not important to you, you can simply leave the default setting "No style sheet" here. In this section, we can also change the size of the icons for the commands. It is best to use the "Medium (24px)" setting here if it is not already selected.

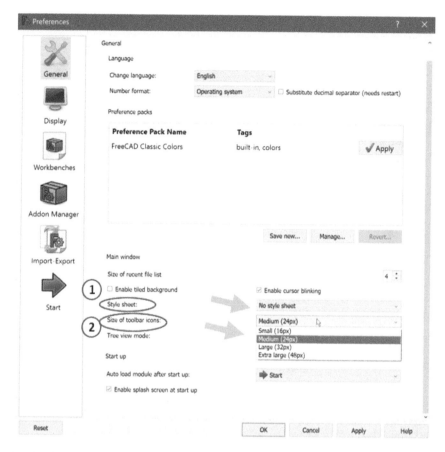

Another important setting from the section "General" we can find in the tab "Units". Here we can set our preferred system of units. We use the standard units "Standard (mm/kg/s/degree)".

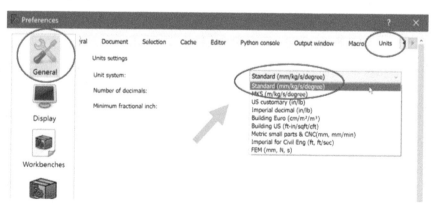

Finally, we have to check in the "Display" area whether the coordinate system is displayed. For this, the option "Show coordinate system in the corner" must be checked.

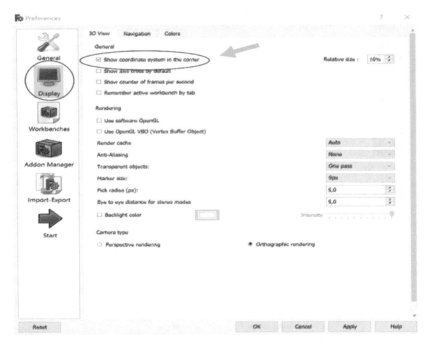

In addition, we can still change the background of the workspace here in the tab "Colors". However, you don't have to do this, it's a matter of taste. For example, we change the background to the color white.

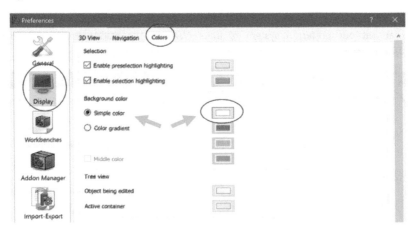

If you have changed settings, click on "Apply" in the lower part of the window and then on the "OK" button to apply the made settings and close the window.

2.2 "FreeCAD" Program environment

In this section, we will have a look at the program environment of "FreeCAD".

2.2.1 Home page

When we launch "FreeCAD", the home page is displayed, which includes three different tabs ("Documents", "Help", "Activity").

"Documents": This tab contains the last used files. It also contains the option "Create new ..." to create a new document. In addition, we can find a few sample files in the lower area.

"Help": This tab contains instructions about the program and how to solve problems. For example, we can search here for a command we want to use in "FreeCAD" and get help on it.

"Activity": This tab shows the last used activities in "FreeCAD". It shows the modification or addition of "FreeCAD" source code and is not relevant for beginners at this time.

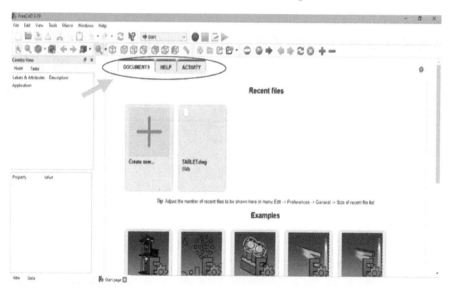

2.2.2 Workspace

Now let's take a look at the working area of the software. In this area, we are about to start our first drawing exercises. Before that, we will open a sample file from the lower part of the tab "Documents" in the section "Examples".

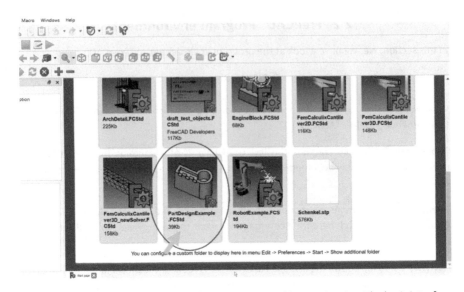

The workspace or drawing area is used to create a new object or drawing. The basic interface includes toolbars, various commands and windows.

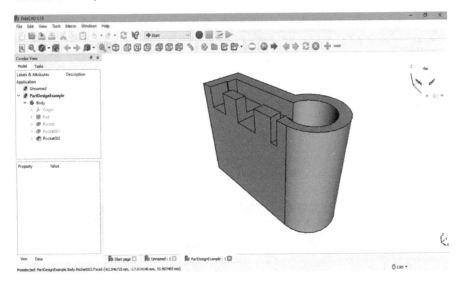

On the left side of the workspace, there is the combo view, which is divided into two tabs.

The "Model" tab shows you the content and structure of your object in the upper area and the properties (parameters) of each selected element in the lower area. In this part browser, you will find the commands that were used to create the 3D object. In this case, for example, various sketches and commands such as "Pad" and "Pocket". But we will get to that later.

Furthermore, the origin and layers of the file are displayed. For displaying, you have to click on the arrow icon to the extension.

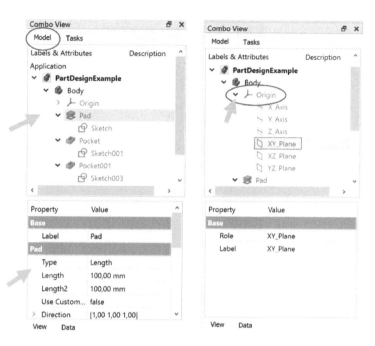

The "Tasks" tab informs you about tasks you need to perform for the design or about the specific parameters of the tool you are currently using.

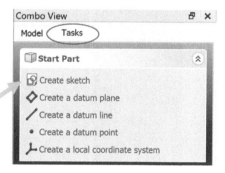

There is also a report view and a Python console in "FreeCAD", which are hidden by default. In the report view you get information, warnings or errors listed, which can make troubleshooting easier. The Python console allows you to watch in real time how the commands and functions you select are executed by program code.

The following steps can be used to enable the report view and the Python console.

Step 1: Enter the "View" menu

Step 2: Click on "Panels"

Step 3: Click on "Report view" and "Python console"

A window will then open in the lower section of the workspace.

However, as a beginner you will rarely need these two windows or, as mentioned before, only for troubleshooting. We can therefore close these two windows again so that we have more space in the work area.

3 The basic workspaces in "FreeCAD"

3.1 General information

In "FreeCAD" there are different workspaces, each designed for a specific task area. You can find them in the drop-down menu to the left of the red circle. The software "FreeCAD" offers numerous workspaces. This can easily confuse a beginner. However, if you want to use "FreeCAD" to create 2D and 3D designs, as well as to make technical drawings, then the workspaces "Part Design", "Sketcher" as well as "TechDraw" are sufficient. We will look at the use of these three workspaces in detail in this beginner's course. In addition, we will take a look at how to assemble individual parts into an assembly. For this, we need to import the workspace "Assembly (A2plus)". But more about that later.

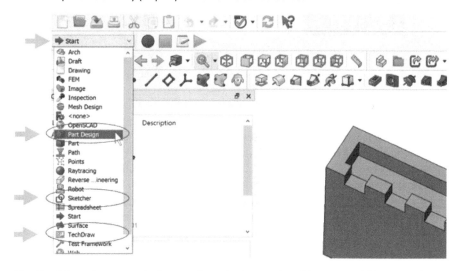

The "Draft" workspace - which we will not look at in detail here - would be used if you wanted to create purely two-dimensional objects. In the "Sketcher" area, you can also create two-dimensional sketches. Since you can later turn these into 3D models, instead of the "Draft" area, let's look at the more suitable "Sketcher" area. The workspace "Part Design" is needed for the creation of three-dimensional objects. This would also be possible with the workspace "Part", but "Part Design" is generally more suitable. Finally, the "TechDraw" area is needed if you want to create technical drawings, i.e., documents with which the designed part can be manufactured.

As you hopefully remember from one of the first chapters, if we intend to create a three-dimensional object, we must first create a 2D sketch. We then transform this 2D sketch into a 3D object using various commands.

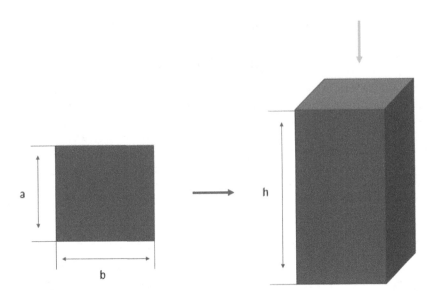

"FreeCAD" now offers us several workspaces to create such a 2D sketch. We can draw a two-dimensional sketch both in the "Draft" area and in the "Sketcher" area. The "Draft" area is only for pure 2D objects, which means you would select this workspace if you wanted to draw a purely two-dimensional object. You could also create a 3D object from a sketch from the "Draft" area, but this approach is not ideal. If you already know that you want to create a 3D object from a 2D sketch, it is better to choose the "Sketcher" workspace. This workspace is ideal for drawing 2D sketches that you will later turn into a 3D object.

So, we could make a sketch for our first 3D object in the "Sketcher" area. But to learn the design with "FreeCAD" as easy as possible, we will start right away in the parent workspace "Part Design". In this workspace, 3D objects can be created. Moreover, in this workspace there is also a function called "Create Sketch", which is a link to the workspace "Sketcher" and with which we can draw our 2D sketch for our 3D object.

The program "FreeCAD" can be a bit confusing here, unfortunately, because there are so many different workspaces. But you just need to remember that as a beginner for a 3D design, we can always start in the "Part Design" area. I will guide you step by step below with a structured approach to creating a 3D model. To do this, we start in the work area "Part Design", then switch to the area "Sketcher" for the 2D sketch and then back to the area "Part Design" for the 3D model. The areas are linked to each other, so this is uncomplicated. But more about that in a moment!

3.2 The "Part Design" Workspace - Part 1: General Information

Before we create our first 3D object, let's get a brief overview of the basic functions of the "Part Design" workspace.

Note: If not all toolbars are displayed as shown here, you have to activate the missing toolbars in the menu bar at the tab "View" in the subgroup "Toolbars". Here you can also deactivate toolbars if necessary.

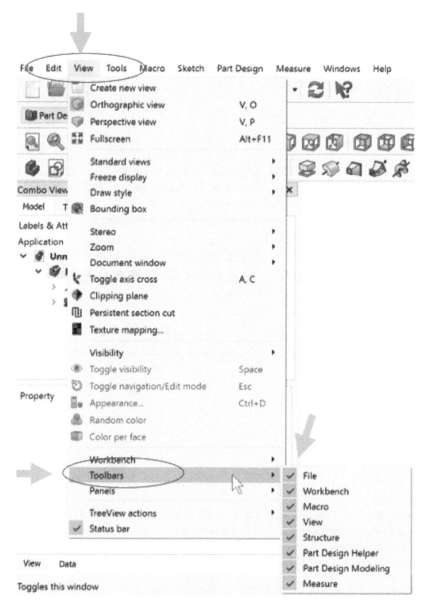

In the upper-left area we find two important functions. First, we can use the function "Fit all" to fit all objects that are in our 3D space into the view. This function is useful, for example, if one or more objects are located very far away. These are then zoomed to a size that is advantageous for the view.

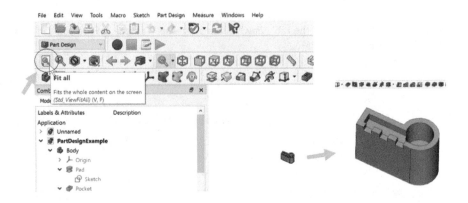

With the function "Draw Style" we can change the display representation of the 3D object. For example, we could select the "Wireframe" option and get a wireframe of our object. Feel free to try the other display options as well.

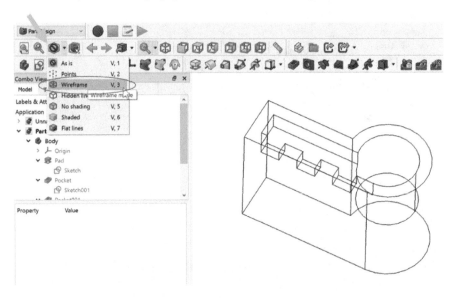

In the middle area of the previous toolbar, we can choose between different views. We can choose to display the isometric view and look at the top face, the bottom face, the front face, the back face or the side faces. These choices are useful when we want to look 100% vertically to one face of the object.

If we can't be that precise, we can of course rotate and move our object with the PC mouse. We will learn how this works in a moment.

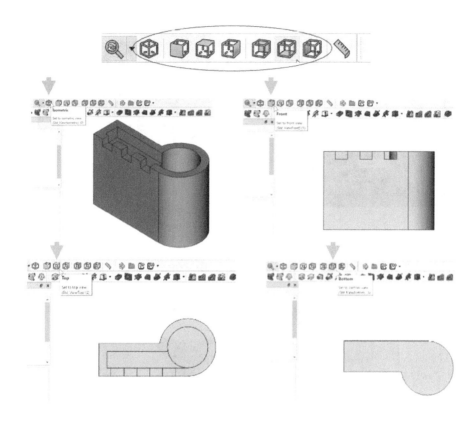

Almost all the functions from the toolbar below will be discussed in detail in the 3D construction, so we will leave them out here. We will only look at the measurement functions here.

Using the function "Measure Linear" we can display the distance between two surfaces or even between two edges. To do this, we simply select the command and then click on the first geometry (for example, the left rear edge of the object) and then directly on the second geometry (for example, the front edge of the object). The dimension is then displayed to us with the help of an arrow.

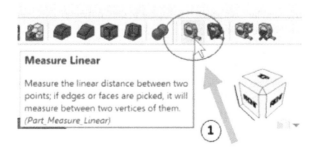

Measure Linear

Measure the linear distance between two points; if edges or faces are picked, it will measure between two vertices of them.
(Part_Measure_Linear)

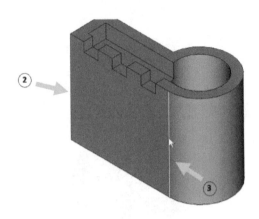

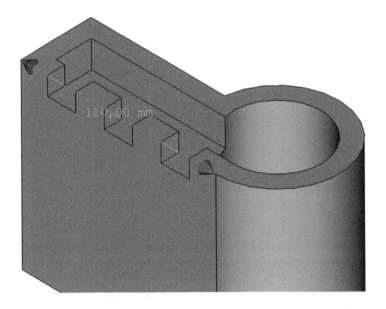

With "Measure Angular" we can also display angles between two elements. This works identically to "Measure Linear".

With "Refresh" we can update all the dimensions after making a change in the geometry.

And with "Clear all" we can delete all displayed dimensions again. We cannot change the values of the dimensions here, we will see how that works in a moment. We will now look in detail at how to create a 3D object.

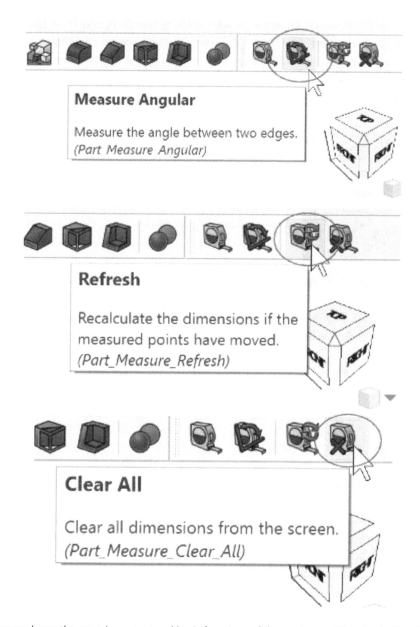

Measure Angular

Measure the angle between two edges.
(Part Measure Angular)

Refresh

Recalculate the dimensions if the measured points have moved.
(Part_Measure_Refresh)

Clear All

Clear all dimensions from the screen.
(Part_Measure_Clear_All)

Now we know the most important and basic functions of the workspace "Part Design" and in the next step we can deal in detail with how to create a 2D sketch and how to then transform this 2D sketch into a 3D object.

The procedure for creating our first 3D object is now as follows. First, we close the sample project. Then, we select "Create new ..." on the start page to create a new document.

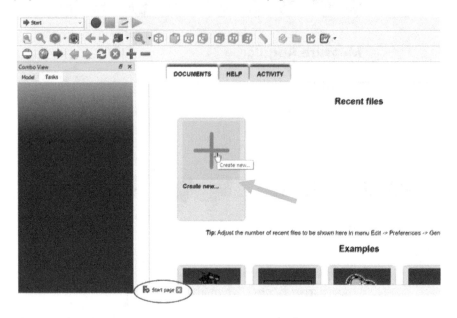

Then we select the workspace "Part Design" from the drop-down menu.

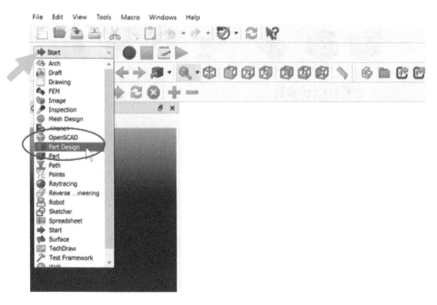

Now, to start with our 3D object, we click on the command "Create Body" in the combo view in the area "Tasks".

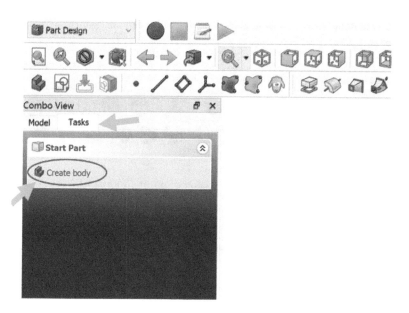

Then, in the "Tasks" area, the creation of a sketch is suggested to us. As you can see, the "Tasks" area can thus serve us - especially at the beginning - as a kind of recipe for our design.

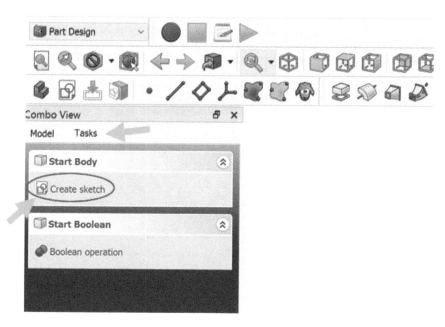

Alternatively, by the way, we could create the body and the 2D sketch using the icons from the command bar. For example, we could also have selected the commands "Create Sketch"

and "Create Body" from the menu bar at the very top of the tab "Sketch" as well as "Part Design".

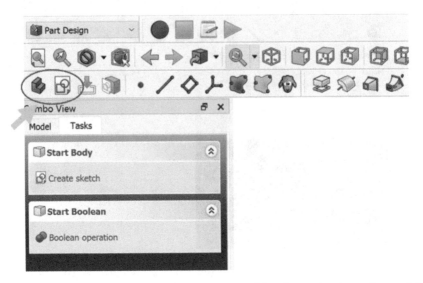

After selecting the "Create sketch" command, we will be shown the three planes of the coordinate system to choose from. We want to create a sketch in two-dimensional space as a basis for our 3D object, so we have to tell the program on which two-dimensional plane we would like to create the sketch. Since a coordinate system of the 3D space has the three axes x, y and z, the three planes x-y, x-z and y-z are available by combining two axis directions each.

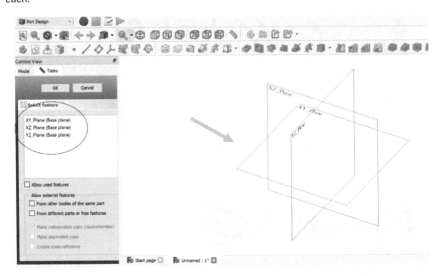

Which layer we select here only influences the later alignment of the object for now. So, for example, we simply select the x-y plane once and confirm with "OK".

This will take us to the plane and at the same time the program will automatically take us to the workspace "Sketcher", which is intended for 2D sketching. As explained at the beginning, a 2D sketch for a 3D object is primarily made in this workspace. As you can see now, the program automatically leads us into this workspace and later on out of it. That is, the area "Sketcher" is linked to the area "Part Design".

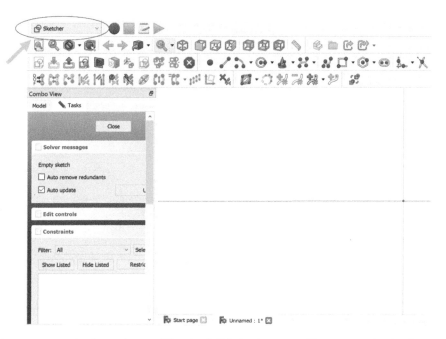

So, we are now in the workspace "Sketcher". This is where we will create our 2D sketch. In the next section, we will get to know this workspace and its commands and functions with the help of sketching exercises. After that, we will come back to the workspace "Part Design" to learn how to create a 3D object from the 2D sketch.

3.3 The "Sketcher" Workspace: Creating a 2D sketch

3.3.1 General and important settings

In the workspace "Sketcher" we create our 2D sketch. This can be thought of as drawing a few lines, rectangles, and circles in the familiar "Paint" program. However, there are a few differences.

Before we start, we make a few settings in the options regarding the display. We do this as usual in the menu bar "Edit" and the selection of "Preferences". Now we navigate in the options to the section "Sketcher".

Here we activate - if desired - the drawing grid by setting a check mark at the option "Show grid". In addition, we can activate that the cursor can more easily select the corner points of the grid, we do this with the option "Grid snap". Also, the grid size can be set here. However, these settings are not mandatory, but only an optional help when drawing.

On the other hand, it is important that in the tab "Colors", we set the fields circled in red to the color black or a similar dark color if we have chosen a white or light background. Otherwise, we would not be able to see the geometric elements later.

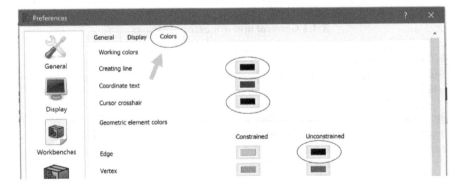

Then we take a look at the drawing plane. In the upper-right area, we see the orbit cube ("navigation cube"), which shows us in which view of the 3D space we are currently located. Currently, this is set to "Top", i.e., we are looking down on the plane from above. We can also rotate or pan the view with this cube. In the lower-right area is a small coordinate system that shows us the orientation based on the axes. We are on the x-y plane, so the y-axis is shown vertically, and the x-axis is shown horizontally. These axes are also shown to us in the same color (green and red) on the drawing plane as a vertical and a horizontal line.

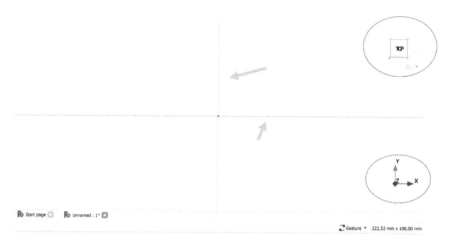

If the display of these two elements is too small for you, you can also change the size in the settings. To achieve this, you need to go to the "Display" area. To make the settings, first switch to the tab "3D View" and then to the tab "Navigation".

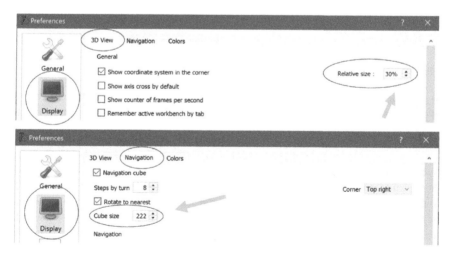

You can move the drawing area and also later the 3D object, depending on the preselected mode. You can select this mode at the bottom right. It is best to select the mode "CAD". The navigation is then as shown. "Pan" means move, by the way. "Rotate", "Zoom" and "Select" should be clear.

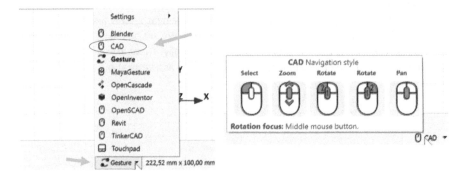

3.3.2 Geometric elements for creating a 2D sketch

Then we can deal with the available geometries that we can use to draw the base surface of our later object. We can find them in the toolbar of "FreeCAD" in the middle area. Here are a variety of basic drawing elements, such as points, lines, circles, rectangles, polygons, etc., are available for selection.

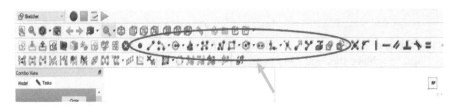

The 2D sketch should correspond, for example, to the cross-section of the desired 3D object or, in the case of simple objects, to the upper surface of the object - i.e. in the case of a cylinder, for example, a circle.

By selecting the command "Create Line", for example, a geometry can be formed from line-shaped elements. Let's try this out. To do this, simply click on any point, e.g., on the center of the coordinate system and start a drawing by clicking and dragging with your mouse. With another click, e.g., on a grid point of the drawing plane, you can define the end of the line.

If you move the cursor in such a way that the line would become horizontal or also vertical, then a small red symbol is shown to you in each case. This symbol is a constraint, which helps to define a sketch completely. In this case it says, for example, that the line will be created conditionally horizontally or vertically. In addition, in this case, it also shows the symbol of a quarter circle with a point on it. This is also a constraint that defines the end point of the line on the coordinate axis. We will come to the constraints in detail in a moment.

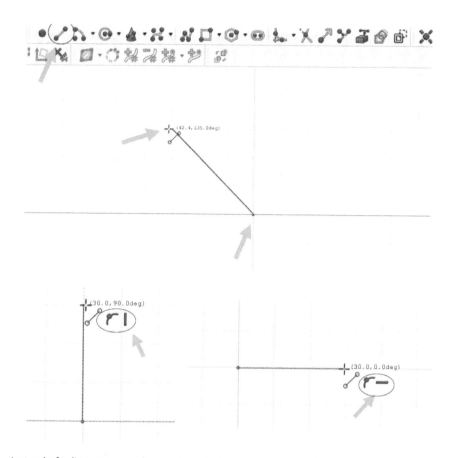

Instead of a line, you can also create a circle, an arc, a rectangle, a polygon or an oblong hole, and much more. Let's try this out one by one.

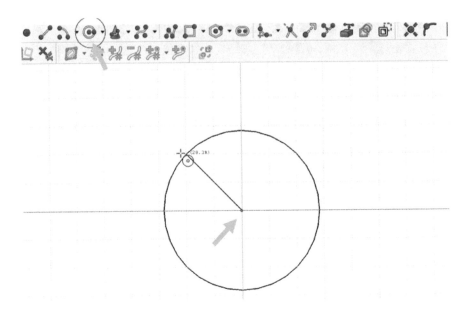

For the arc, we first select the center point, then the start point of the arc, and then the end point of the arc.

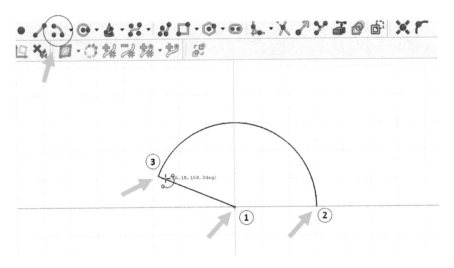

With the rectangle, you can choose between a normal rectangle, a centered rectangle or a rounded rectangle. Try all three options, and you will quickly see what the differences are.

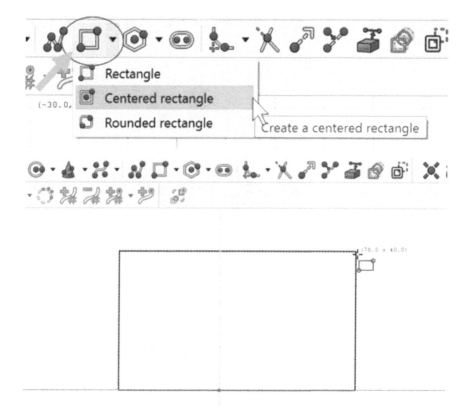

By the way, this selection option is also available for the geometry elements: Circle, Arc and Polygon. Feel free to try out all the selection options independently here as well.

With the command "Polygon" you can quickly create a triangle, a pentagon or a hexagon without having to compose it from individual lines. You specify the center of the circumscribed circle and then select an end point in the drawing plane.

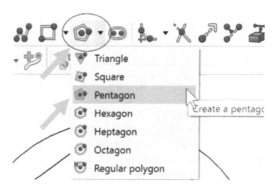

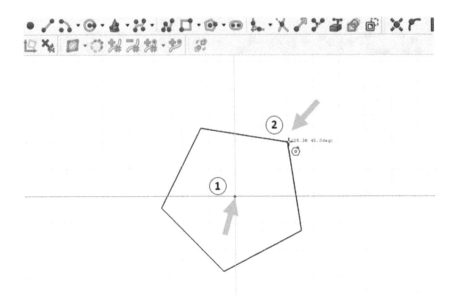

Very useful is also the command "Slot", with which you can draw an oblong hole in a quick and easy way. You simply select a start point and an end point, which represent the respective center of the two semicircles, and the slot is created.

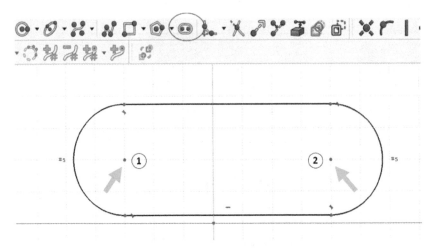

The other elements you can create here are: Point, Polyline, "B-Spline" and Elliptical geometries. You won't need these elements as often as a beginner, but you can still try them out once each. By the way, the polyline is simply a chain of lines and the "B-Spline" command creates a freeform curve. For these two elements, simply select several different points in the drawing plane and end the chain with either the right mouse button or the "ESC" key.

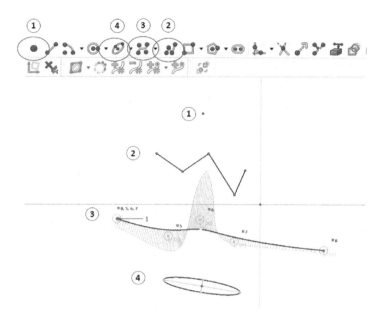

3.3.3 Modifying a 2D sketch

After we have created a sketch, we can modify it if necessary. For this purpose, we will deal with two important functions. These are the functions "Fillet" and "Trim edge".

The function "Fillet" can be used to round edges. To do this, we draw, for example, a "Centered rectangle", whose center should be congruent with the coordinate origin.

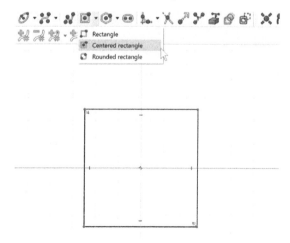

After that, we click on the function "Fillet" and then select two edges one after the other.

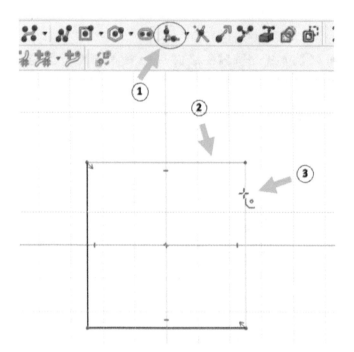

The program then creates a fillet for the corner of the two edges.

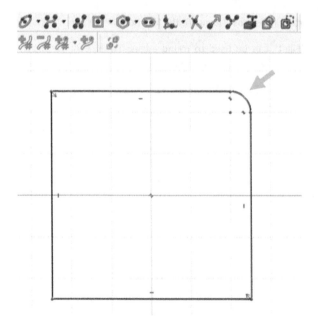

With the function "Trim Edge" you can remove superfluous lines. Let's take a look at what this means. We will draw two circles that intersect each other.

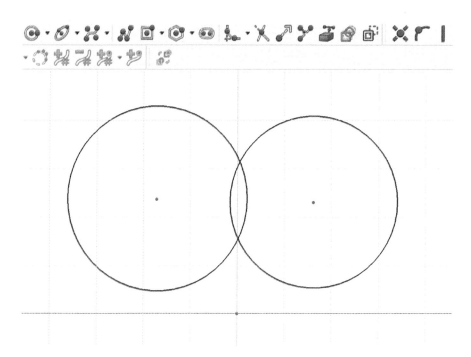

If we now want to connect these two circles, we can use the function "Trim Edge" to quickly and easily remove the two middle segments of the circles. We do this by selecting the function and then clicking one after the other on the segments we wish to remove.

We then get a circle that is connected at the corner points. The program creates the necessary connections automatically with this function.

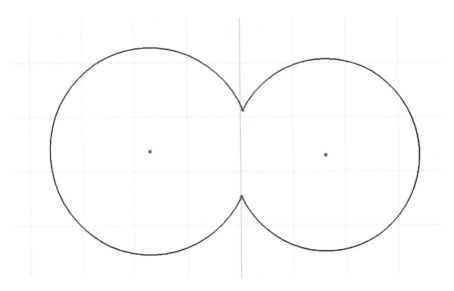

3.3.4 The constraints

To create a three-dimensional object, it is important that the sketch is completely closed and has no gaps. So - at least as a beginner - we always need a surface whose vertices are connected. In addition, the sketch must be completely defined. Completely defined means that the sketched geometry is fixed on the 2D plane and cannot be moved. Such a fixation can be done by constraints.

Earlier, it was mentioned that the small red symbols that appear during drawing creation are such constraints. You can find a lot of constraints in the command bar of "FreeCAD". With a click on the small arrow on the far right, you can display all of them.

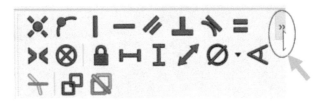

We will now look at the most important conditions in detail.

In "FreeCAD" you can also find dimensions under constraints. You can define a sketch completely by dimensions, or combine dimensions and other constraints. Let's take a look at an example. For example, if we draw a rectangle, we can first define the length and the width of the rectangle using the commands "Constrain vertical distance" and "Constrain horizontal distance".

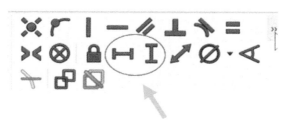

We do this by first selecting the respective constraint and then the line of the rectangle that we want to dimension. A window appears in which we can enter a dimension, e.g., 40 mm for the width and 30 mm for the height of the rectangle.

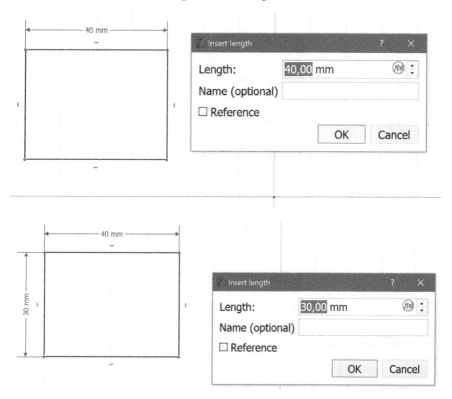

If we now click on the rectangle with the cursor and move it at the same time, we can see that the sketch is not yet completely defined, since the rectangle can still be moved in the drawing plane.

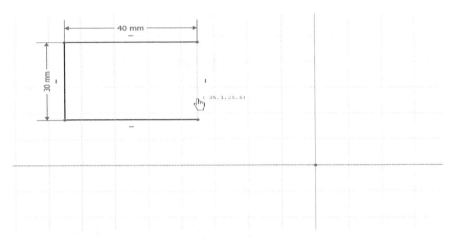

To obtain a completely defined sketch, we can prevent this possibility of displacement either by adding further dimensions to a fixed point (e.g., to the origin), or alternatively by adding another constraint.

1st option: Add two more dimensions (We need one dimension in x-direction and one in y-direction).

We add one vertical and one horizontal dimension each from the lower-right corner of the rectangle to the coordinate origin. We do this in the same way as we dimension the rectangle. For example, we can choose 20 mm each.

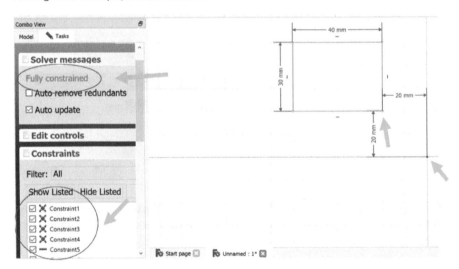

After we have created the dimensions, the lines of the rectangle turn green. This color change tells us that the sketch element is now fully defined. You can also see this in the combo view on the left side by the label "Fully constrained". In addition, all constraints that are in the sketch are displayed here, a little further down.

2nd option: Use another constraint.

As an alternative to dimensioning, we can also use another constraint to completely define the sketch. For example, we use the constraint "Constrain coincident", i.e., congruent. After deleting the previously created dimensions, we first click on the constraint and then successively on the corner point of the rectangle and the coordinate origin.

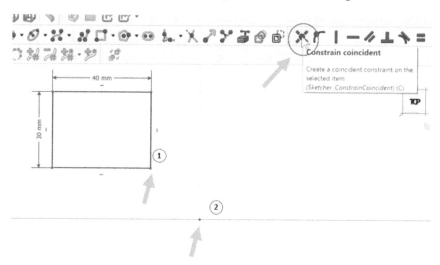

These two points are then fixed as congruent and the sketch turns green.

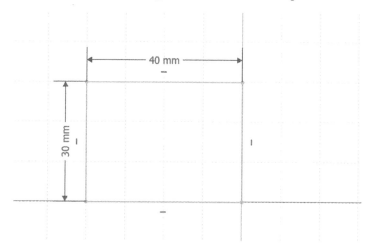

There are many other constraints, which are slightly different depending on the CAD program, but most of them are almost identical or even have the same name. We will now take a detailed look at the most important constraints of "FreeCAD".

The constraint "Coincident":

We have just learned about this constraint. This command is used to connect two different points congruently.

For example, draw two different lines with the command "Line". Then first click on the "Constrain Coincident" condition, and then select the two upper endpoints of the lines one after the other to connect them.

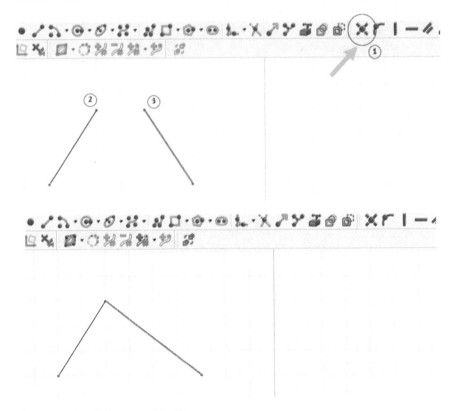

The constraint "Point onto object":

This command is used to connect a point of an object congruently with the geometry of another object. The difference with the previous command is that it does <u>not</u> connect two points, but a point with an object (e.g., a circle).

For clarification, we draw a circle around the previous geometry. Then we select the command, the upper corner point of the lines and the circle one after the other.

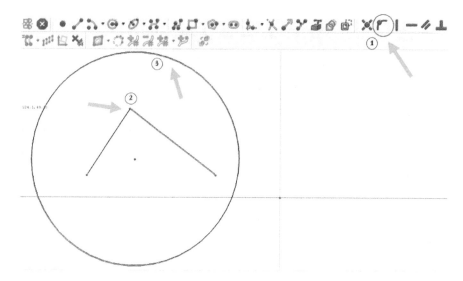

The vertex is connected to the circle, and it is noticeable that the diameter of the circle changes. This is the case because we have not dimensioned the circle, and therefore it is not completely defined and can therefore move freely on the plane.

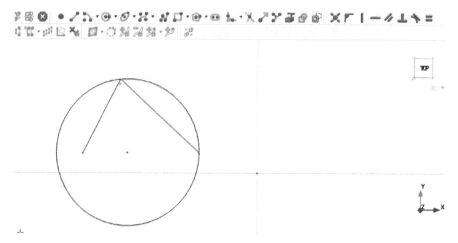

By the way: If we had completely dimensioned or defined the circle, then the diameter of the circle would not have changed, but the line geometry would have changed the position so that the constraint can be fulfilled. If we had completely defined both geometries (line geometry and circle), then the constraint would no longer have been possible because the geometry elements would then no longer have been able to change the position. You are welcome to try this out on your own so that you understand the relationships even better! You can dimension the circle with the constraint "Constrain arc or circle". For example, select "Constrain diameter" from the drop-down menu and click on the circle.

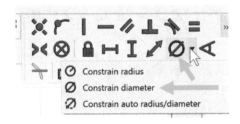

The constraints "Constrain vertically" and "Constrain horizontally":

These two commands are used to make an element either vertical or horizontal. For example, we draw two diagonal lines. Then we first click on "Constrain vertically" and select the lower line. Then we click on "Constrain horizontally" and select the upper line.

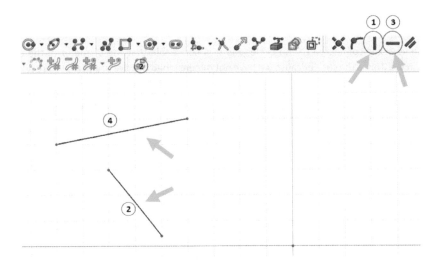

We get a horizontal and a vertical line. We can also see this from the small red symbols.

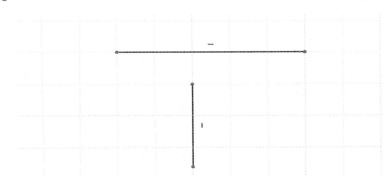

The constraint "Constrain parallel":

This command is used to create two parallel lines. For this, we need two lines that are <u>not</u> parallel. After we have created the lines, we click on the command and then on both lines one after the other. It does not matter which line we select first.

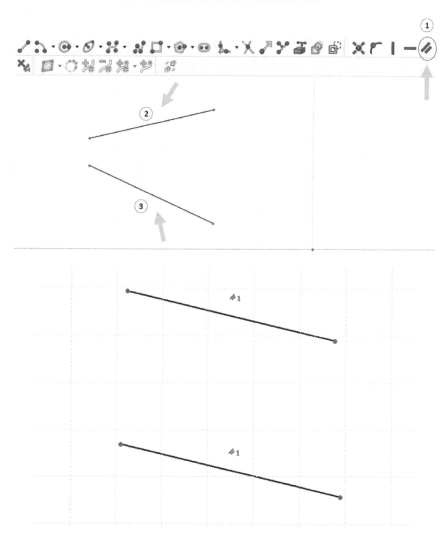

The constraint "Constrain perpendicular":

This command is used to set a line perpendicular to another line. For example, we draw a horizontal line and a diagonal line. For the constraint, we then select the command "Constrain Perpendicular" and then click on both lines one after the other.

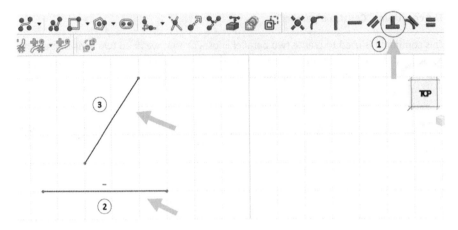

The constraint "Constrain tangent":

For example, if we want to draw a line tangent to a circle shape, we use the command "Constrain tangent". We draw a circle and a line (outside the circle). Then we select the command, and then we click on the line and then on the edge of the circle.

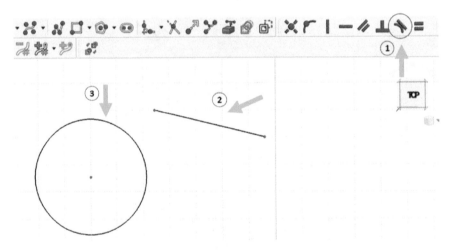

The line is now fixed tangentially to the circle. This becomes clearer when you try to move the line.

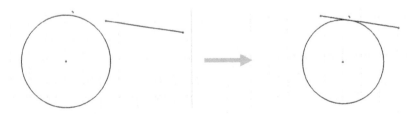

The constraint "Constrain equal":

With this command, you can make two elements of different dimensions (e.g., : lines or even circles) identical. We can try this with two circles of different size and two lines of different length. We select the command and then click first on one of the two circles and then on the other.

The execution of the condition in this case depends on which element we click first. If we click the smaller circle first and then the larger circle, we will get two small circles. On the other hand, if we select the larger circle first and then the smaller circle, we will get two large circles. The procedure is the same for lines.

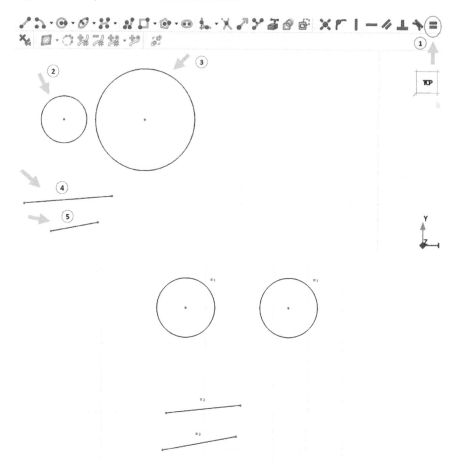

The constraint "Constrain symmetrical":

This command is used to align two points of an element symmetrically according to a reference line. For example, we draw three lines. The middle line represents our reference line, we want to set the two upper corner points of the outer lines symmetrical to this line.

To do this, we first select the command "Constrain symmetrical" and then click successively on the two upper corner points of the outer lines and then on the middle reference line.

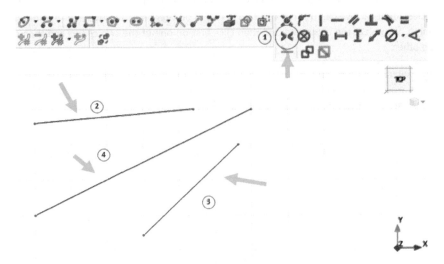

The vertices are then fixed with equal distance and on a perpendicular to the reference line. We can also turn the reference line into a construction geometry - a kind of auxiliary line. By clicking on the line and selecting "Toggle construction geometry" the line will be colored blue. This can also be undone with the same command. This procedure improves the clarity of a construction. In 3D mode, the program ignores these geometries.

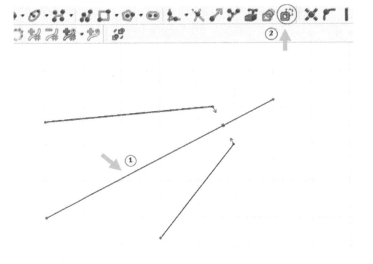

The constraint "Constrain angle":

With the command "Constrain angle" we can define the angle between two elements. This command is important if we want to dimension a geometry. Besides a pure length dimension, we can also define a geometry with the help of angles.

For example, we draw a triangle using the command "Create Polyline". Now we can define the three interior angles of the triangle using the constraint "Constrain angle".

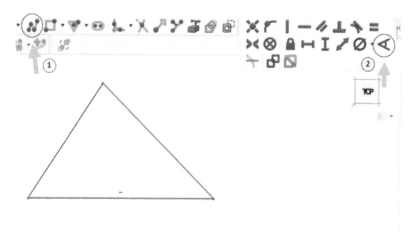

We then always click on two lines adjacent to each other and enter the desired angle, e.g., 60° each. We have to do this exactly twice, the program calculates the third angle automatically from the other two and the interior angle sum of a triangle (180°). Not only that, but we cannot define this angle any more, otherwise the sketch would be overdetermined. Overdetermined means that too many constraints have been set which interfere with each other, exclude each other or are redundant - i.e. superfluous.

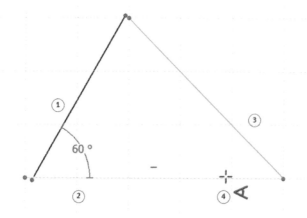

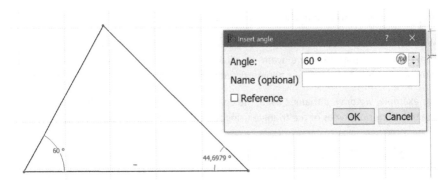

Now we know the main constraints and geometric elements to draw our first 2D sketch, which we can then transform into a 3D object in the "Part Design" workspace.

For example, we draw a rectangle that should be centered on the coordinate origin. To do this, we use the command "Centered rectangle" and select the coordinate origin as the starting point. With a movement with our PC mouse, we stretch the rectangle.

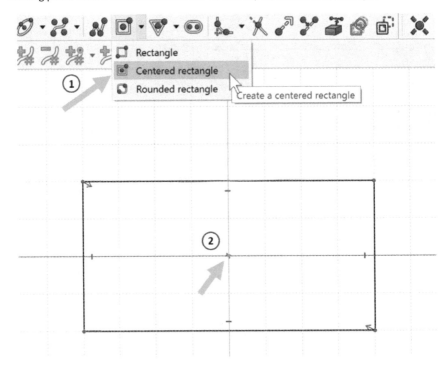

For the sketch to be completely defined, we still need two dimensions for the rectangle. For this, we use the two constraints "Constrain horizontal distance" and "Constrain vertical distance", as we learned before. For example, we can assign the two dimensions 40 mm and 80 mm.

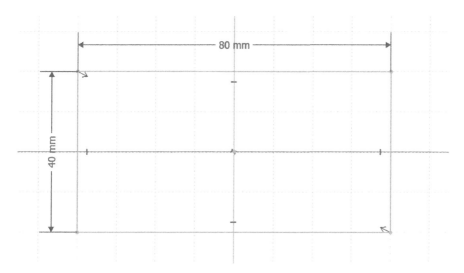

Since we had already connected the center of the rectangle to the coordinate origin when we drew it, we do not need any further constraints, since the position in the plane has already been fixed in this way. We can see this again from the green color of our geometry, which tells us that the sketch is completely defined.

To create a 3D object from this 2D sketch, we switch to the workspace "Part Design". We do this by clicking on the icon "Leave sketch" from the toolbar in the upper-left corner, or by clicking on the button "Close" in the combo view.

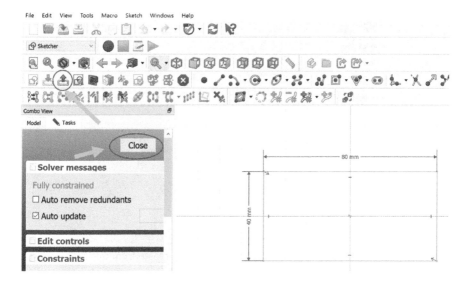

After closing the sketch, we are in the workspace "Part Design" and we see the sketch in the combo view in the tab "Model" in the part browser.

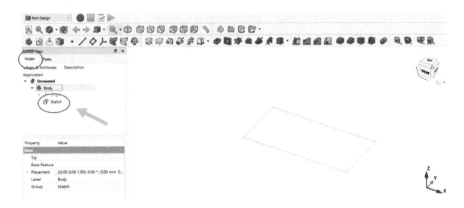

By double-clicking on it, we can edit the sketch again, we will return to the workspace "Sketcher".

With a right click on it, we can also edit the sketch and copy, delete, make display settings and much more!

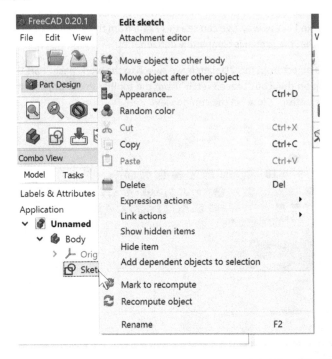

Now please think for a moment what 3D object we could create from this rectangular 2D sketch.

3.4 The "Part Design" Workspace - Part 2: 3D Modeling

Now that we have created a 2D sketch on one plane of the coordinate system, we can create a 3D object from it. We create a simple cuboid from our rectangular sketch.

To create a 3D object from a 2D sketch, there are a few modeling tools in the CAD software that can be divided into two groups. Using the commands from the first group, the additive tools, you can add material to a sketch, or to an existing 3D object. You can think of this process as using a 3D printer or imagine that you are making pottery. Using the commands from the second group, the subtractive tools, you can remove material from a 3D object. This can be thought of as machining a component, for example, using mechanical processes such as turning, milling, or drilling.

3.4.1 Additive tools

The tool "Pad":

One of the most important additive tools is the tool "Pad". This tool is similar to the "Extrude" or "Extrusion" tool known from other CAD programs. Thanks to this command it is possible to extrude a 2D sketch linearly, i.e., to add material in the form of the sketch geometry in the direction of the axis. That is why this command is sometimes called Extrude Linear "Extrude Linear".

We use this command to create a cuboid from our 2D sketch. For this, the sketch must be selected in the part browser. Then we can either switch to the area "Tasks", here available tools are displayed directly, or select the button "Pad" in the toolbar.

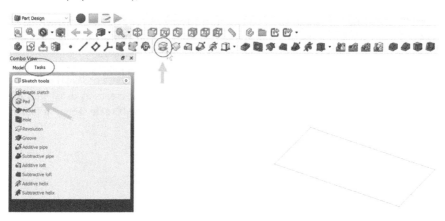

As soon as we have selected the command, the preview of the box is generated. In the section "Tasks" in the combo view, we find the settings for the command "Pad". These settings are specific for each modeling tool and therefore different. For the "Pad" tool, we can enter the desired dimension in extrusion direction at "Length", here e.g., 10 mm.

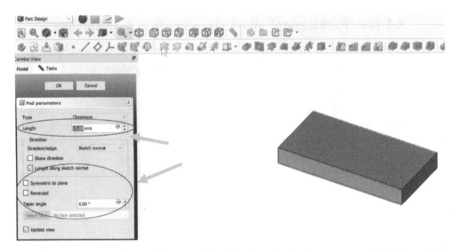

In addition, we can change the extrusion direction in the lower area. With the option "Symmetric to plane" the origin of the 3D object would be placed directly on the sketch plane. This means the extrusion would be created 5 mm up and 5 mm down for a 10 mm dimension. Without this setting, the material will be added 10 mm up. With the "Reversed" option, you could reverse the direction of the extrusion, meaning 10 mm of the material would be added down instead of up. Just try both options, and you will understand it better. Moreover, with the option "Taper angle" we could create a conical shape, you can just try that too.

The tool "Revolution":

With this command, we can turn a 2D sketch into a 3D object by adding material in a rotating motion around an axis. Think of it as if you were making cotton candy. You hold a wooden stick (symbolic of the axis) in a device and the cotton candy is wound up.

We need to create a 2D sketch again for this command. To do this, close or save the file with the cuboid. Then we create a new "Part Design" document and create as usual with the command "Create body" first a body and then with the command "Create sketch" a sketch. For the sketch, we again select the x-y plane.

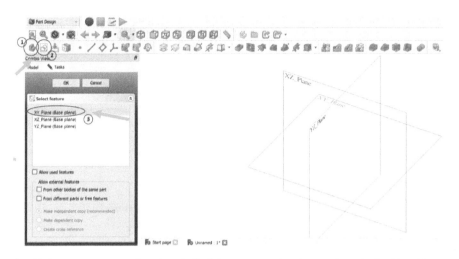

On this layer, we now need to draw half of the cross-sectional area of our desired 3D object. For example, we want to create the blank of an M10 bolt. To achieve this, we first consider what the cross-section of the finished object will look like. To help your spatial imagination, you can take a look at the following figure.

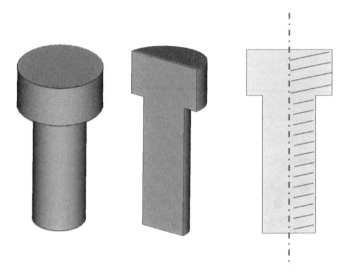

As you can see, the cross-sectional area of the bolt represents a 2D sketch consisting of two rectangular elements. However, to be able to create the bolt with the function "Revolution", we only need one half (hatched area) of the cross-section. We will then mirror this later on the axis (semicolon line).

That is, we need to draw the hatched area on our x-y plane. We do this with the command "Create polyline".

We start for the first line exactly on the coordinate origin and then add the following lines as shown. Finally, we add horizontal and vertical dimensions with the two commands "Constrain horizontal distance" and "Constrain vertical distance".

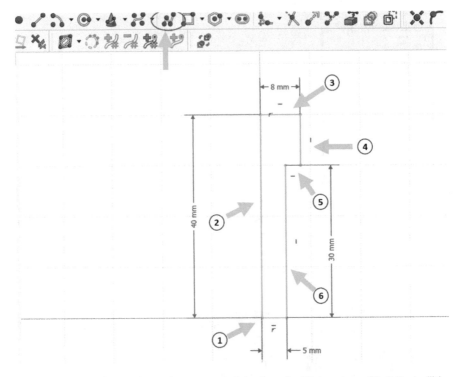

Now our 2D sketch is ready, and we can switch back to the 3D area (area "Part Design") by closing the sketch ("Close" in the combo view).

Then select the command "Revolution". The sketch must be selected in the part browser.

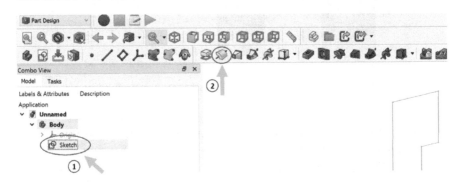

The program automatically selects the axis of rotation and creates the desired 3D body.

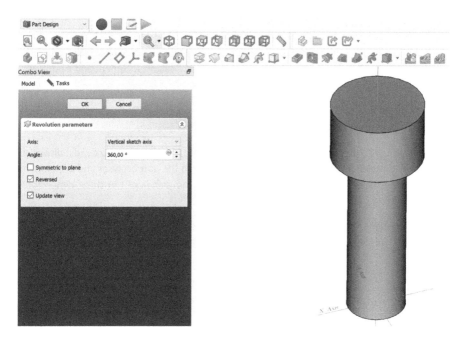

If we do not need a full 360° rotation, but only a partial area, we can specify the angle for the rotation in the combo view in the "Tasks" area.

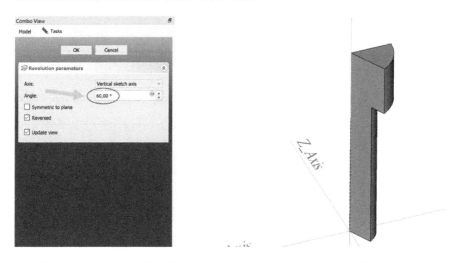

In addition, we could also select the rotation axis manually - at the option "Axis". In our case, we choose the y-axis because we had sketched on the x-y-plane. By the way, this axis is here equivalent to the selection "Vertical sketch axis".

The tool "Additive loft":

With this command, you can create a solid by connecting at least two sketches on planes parallel to each other. To do this, we create a new "Part Design" document and a body with the "Create body" function.

So that we can now create sketches on different planes, we must first create another plane. We do this with the function "Datum plane".

Before we can use the function "Datum plane" to create an offset plane, we must display all the planes by selecting the origin of the created body in the part browser and pressing the space bar on the keyboard. This allows us to show the planes of the three-dimensional space, or later to hide them.

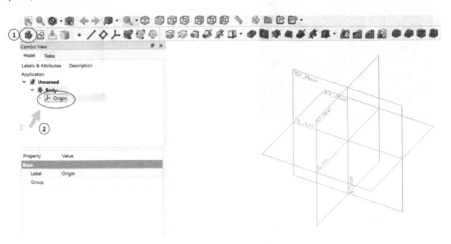

Now we select the body ("Body") in the part browser and then click on the function "Datum plane" in the toolbar.

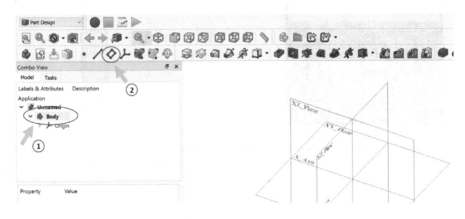

In the combo view, a window appears in which we can make the settings for the new layer. In the first step, we select one of the three default planes that will serve as a reference for our new plane. For example, we select the x-y plane by clicking on it.

After that, we can select the offset of the new plane to the reference plane in the lower area in the combo view. Here we have to enter the offset in x-direction, y-direction and z-direction. Since we only want an offset in z-direction, we enter here e.g., 50 mm. The new plane will then be displayed 50 mm above the x-y plane.

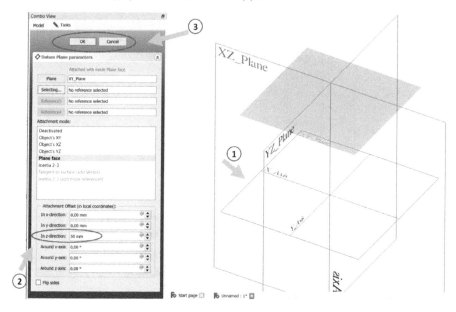

With "OK" we can then create the layer, with "Cancel" we could cancel the process.

In the following, we will create a sketch on the x-y plane as well as on the new plane. We start with the sketch on the x-y plane. For example, we draw a rectangle whose center lies on the coordinate origin and dimension it with 50 mm in width and 30 mm in height.

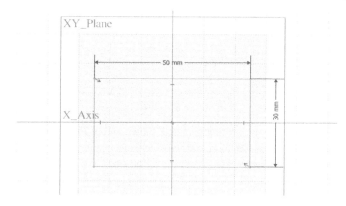

Then we close the sketch and start a new sketch on the previously created offset layer by first clicking on it and then selecting the "Create Sketch" command.

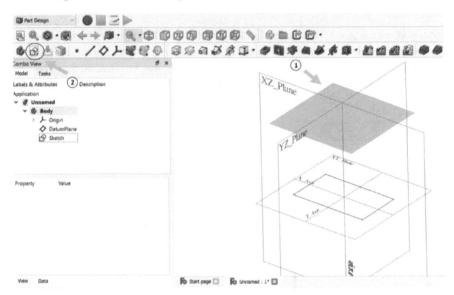

On this layer, we now create a rectangle similar to the one before, only the two dimensions should be swapped, i.e., the rectangle should be 30 mm wide and 50 mm high.

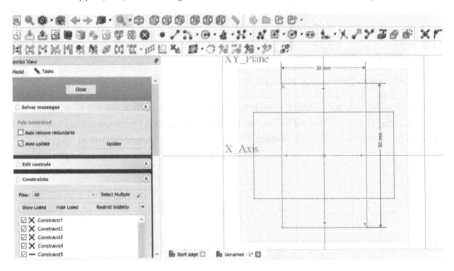

Don't be confused here by the existing rectangle shown in red. That's simply the rectangle we drew earlier on the x-y plane. Now that we're looking at the drawing view from above, we can see it shining through. This is very helpful when you want to construct two interdependent geometries.

After we have closed the sketch, we can hide the layers again with the space bar (1). We can also see the two sketched rectangles floating on top of each other in the drawing area. Now we can use the command "Additive loft". To do this, we first select the two sketches in the part browser one after the other by holding down the CTRL key (2) and then the command in the toolbar (3).

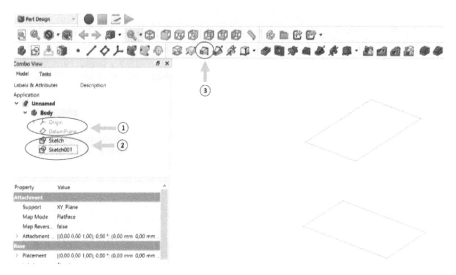

Then the program automatically generates the preview of the desired body, which is a connection of the two 2D sketches. Confirm with "OK" so that the body is also created.

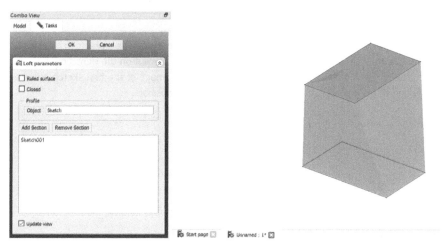

The tool "Additive pipe":

This command is used to connect at least two cross-sections along a path. The path does not have to be straight, it can also be curved. Also, the cross-sections to be connected can have a different shape (e.g., rectangle and circle). This tool is similar to the "Sweep" command known from other CAD programs.

To apply the command, we need two sketches and a path. First, we create the two sketches. These sketches can either be on mutually offset planes, or they can be on the same plane. We create the two sketches on the same plane, and again on the x-y plane. However, be sure to create two separate sketches and do not draw everything in one sketch.

We draw a circle with 20 mm diameter on the x-axis, which we dimension with 60 mm distance to the coordinate origin.

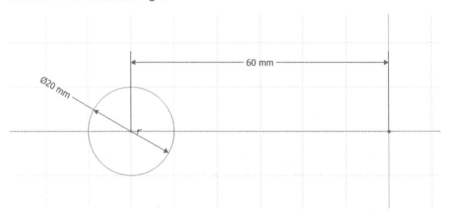

Then we close this first sketch and create a new sketch, also on the x-y plane. In this sketch, we also create a circle with a diameter of 20 mm, but we place it on the right side. Don't be confused by the red circle on the left side, this is just an image of the first sketch. You can easily find this out if you try to click or edit it. This is not possible.

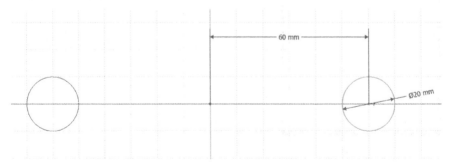

Then we close this second sketch and obtain the following representation.

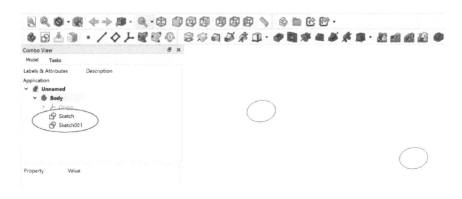

To use the command "Additive Pipe" we need a path. We want to create a handle that looks like this.

To do this, we need a path that connects the centers of the two circles in the x-z plane. Think of it as a wire frame that we will add material to later.

So, we create a new sketch on the x-z plane and draw a semicircle with the function "Center and end points". The center of the arc should be on the coordinate origin. The start point and the end point of the arc should be in the center of each of the two circles sketched before. Since we are in the x-z plane, we see, in a sense, the side view of the two circles. That is, we only see two short red lines lying on the x-axis, which is also red, making it somewhat difficult to see the two centers. Alternatively, we can simply assign a diameter of 120 mm to the arc, and connect the two end points to the x-axis using the constraint "Constrain point onto object".

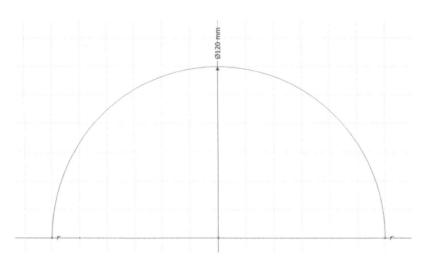

Then we close the sketch and get the following geometry.

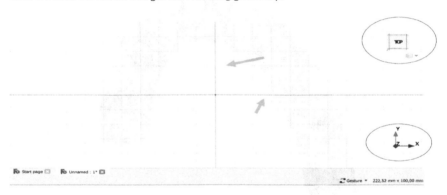

Now we apply the command "Additive Pipe" by first selecting the first sketch as the cross-section geometry and then the command in the toolbar.

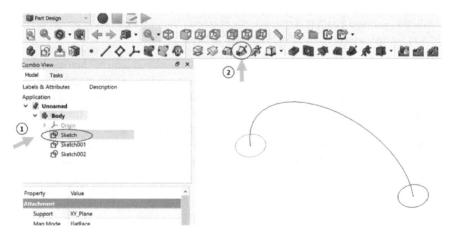

If an error now appears in the lower bar, you can ignore it or click it away. In the next step we check if in the area "Tasks" in the combo view in the menu item "Orientation mode" the option "Standard" is selected and if in the menu item "Transform mode" the option "Constant" is selected. After that, we can click on the button "Object" in the area "Path to sweep along" and select our arc as path for the operation (just click in the drawing plane).

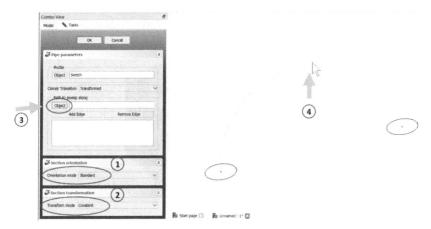

The program will then create the preview of the desired 3D shape.

Lastly, try the other selections at "Orientation mode" and "Transform mode" so you can see what each does. With "OK" you create the body and finish the command.

These were the main additive modeling tools. Now we come to the subtractive tools. As an exercise, please create a cuboid on your own that has a rectangle with a length of 80 mm and a width of 60 mm as its base. The height of the box should then be, for example, 50 mm. Use the commands "Create body", "Create sketch" and "Pad". Make sure that you define the sketch completely (green color).

3.4.2 Subtractive tools

To look at subtractive tooling in detail, let's start with this cuboid because we need a starting material. You can think of it like machining. If you want to use a CNC mill to machine a component, you also need to first clamp a semi-finished product (starting material/raw material) into the machine.

The tool "Pocket":

One of the most important subtractive tools is the "Pocket" tool. This tool is the counterpart of the "Pad" tool. We will use this command to make a cutout, that is, we will use it to remove material from the 3D object. For example, we could make a rectangular cutout in the middle area of the box. To do this, we will create a sketch on the upper side of the box. This time we do not select a plane of the coordinate system for the sketch, but directly a face of the box.

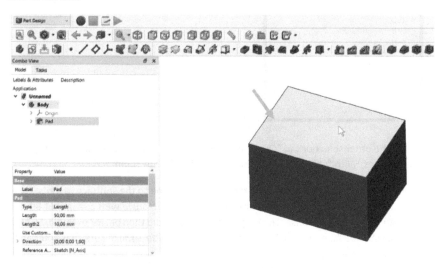

Then, as usual, we automatically reach the "Sketcher" area. Here we can sketch a rectangle on the upper surface of the box. We set the rectangle to the center of the coordinate system and dimension it with 40 mm each so that a square is created. After that, we can close the sketch with "Close".

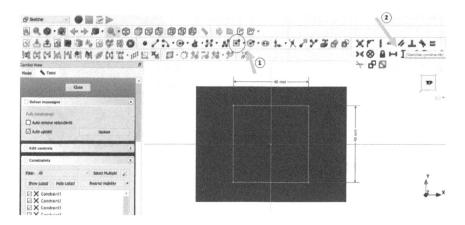

Then, in 3D mode ("Part Design"), we first make sure that the sketch is selected in the Part browser (tab "Model" in the combo view). Then we can select the command "Pocket" from the subtractive tools area.

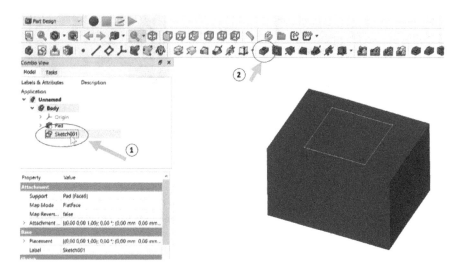

After we have executed the command, the preview of the cutout with the default settings will appear automatically. In our case, the setting "Type" has the option "Dimension" selected by default and the setting "Length" has a dimension of 5 mm entered.

However, we would like the cutout to go through the whole part. On the one hand, we could achieve this by simply entering the height of the box. On the other hand, we can also simply select the option "Through all" in the "Dimension" setting.

With the option "Up to face" we could make the cutout up to a certain face, with the option "To first" up to the next face and with the option "Two dimensions" we could define a cutout in two directions with two different dimensions. However, these options do not make sense in this example. Confirm with "OK" and the section will be created.

The tool "Hole":

Now let's deal with the next tool. With the command "Hole" you can create holes. A hole can also be created with the command "Pocket" (circle as 2D sketch), but the command "Hole" is better suited for this purpose regarding its settings. You can also create and display threads with this command.

To create a hole, we again need a 2D sketch, with which we tell the program at which position the hole should be created. We can do this with a circle. For example, we want to create four M6 threaded holes, so we draw four circles, each 6 mm in diameter, on the top surface of our 3D object. Once we have created a sketch on the top surface of the 3D object, we first draw the four circles and then dimension one of them with a 6 mm diameter. We make the other circles identical to the dimensioned circle with the constraint "Constrain equal", so we save three more dimensions.

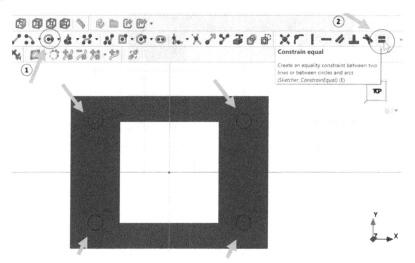

Now we still have to determine the positions of our circles so that the sketch is completely defined. To do this, we first specify all horizontal dimensions (select one circle center and the coordinate origin each) with 30 mm each.

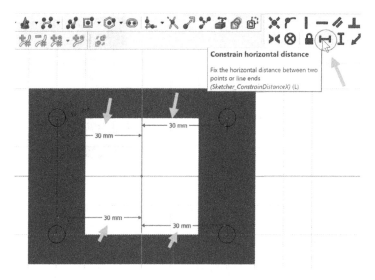

Then we add all vertical dimensions with 20 mm each.

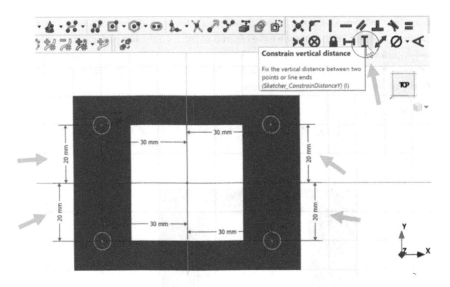

Then all the dimensions are created, and we can close the sketch.

Then we make sure that the 2D sketch we just created is selected in the Part browser, and we can start the "Hole" command.

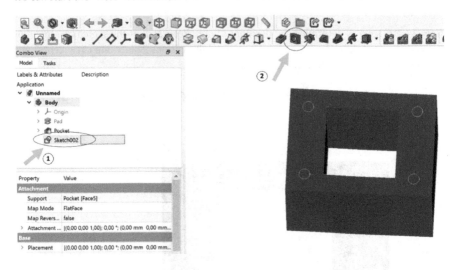

Again, a preview of the drillings is automatically created by the program. In the combo view on the left side in the tab "Tasks" we can make the settings for the holes. Since we want to create threaded holes, we select the option "ISO metric regular profile" in the setting "Profile" and activate the options "Threaded", "Model Thread" and "Update View" so that the thread is displayed modeled in each case (1). Depending on the PC performance, this may take some time.

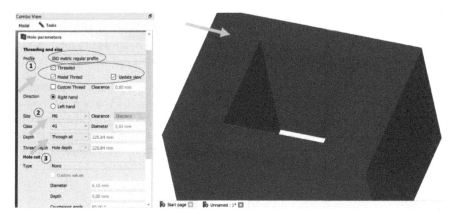

Then we set the size of the thread (2). In the setting "Size" we choose "M6" and in the setting "Depth" we choose the option "Through all" because we want a hole that goes through the whole component (3). If we want a specific length, we could set that here. Then we would select the option "Dimension" instead of "Through all".

In the lower area we find a few more settings, but we do not need them here. For example, we could additionally select the bore angle (2) or the type of bore (1) (e.g., counterbore). If we zoom in close to one of the holes, we can see the modeled thread.

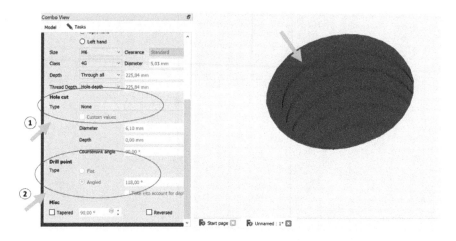

We still confirm with "OK" so that the drillings are also created. This may take some time again, since we are modeling the holes.

Generally, it is recommended to turn off the modeled representation for better performance during design. However, when designing for 3D printing, you need the threads in modeled form.

The tool "Groove":

With the tool "Groove" you can create a section using a rotation. We need a rotation part for this function, i.e., we save our previous 3D object and create a new document.

We then create a simple cylindrical component with a diameter of 30 mm and a height of 100 mm. You can create this cylindrical component in two ways. Do you remember how? Think back to the additive tools. On the one hand, we can use the "Pad" function, but on the other hand, we can use the "Revolution" function. Since we are constructing a rotational part, we simply use the function "Revolution". For example, we draw a rectangle on the x-z plane and dimension it as follows. Note: We need 15 mm as horizontal dimension, because we draw only half.

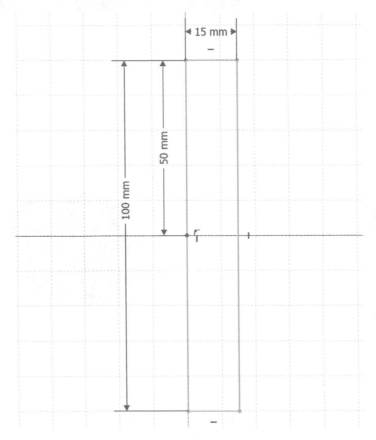

By the way, we can either set a corner of the rectangle to the coordinate origin, or set a 50 mm distance to the coordinate origin as shown here. To define the sketch even more completely, we also set the left vertical line to the coordinate origin with the constraint "Constrain point onto object".

Then we close the 2D sketch and create the 3D body by clicking on the command "Revolution". Confirm with "OK".

For the function "Groove" we now need another 2D sketch that specifies the geometry of the rotated section. For the sketch, we can choose either the x-z plane or the y-z plane of the body.

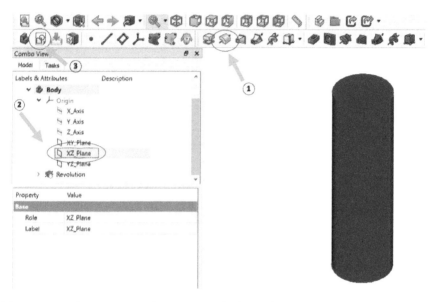

We want to make two rectangular cutouts in the body, these must protrude into the body so that we can remove material later. To do this, we hide the body so that we have a better view of our sketch. We do this by going to the "Model" tab in the combo view of the sketch and right-clicking on the body. We select "Toggle visibility" and the body disappears. Alternatively, we can simply press the space bar.

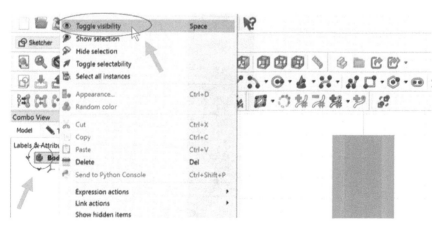

Then we draw two rectangles, which we dimension with 5 mm edge length each, so that squares are created. We also want the two outer edges of the squares to lie on the outer edge of the cylinder, so we need 15 mm here. Finally, we add 30 mm each for the vertical dimensioning.

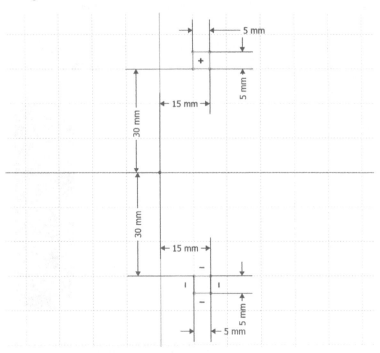

After that, we can show the body again in an identical way using the "Toggle visibility" option. Then we can close the sketch.

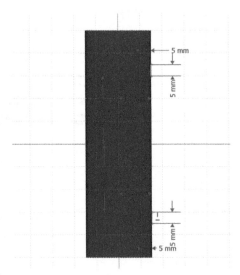

After making sure that the sketch is selected in the Part browser, we can now run the "Groove" command.

The program generates the preview of the two rectangular sections, and we can create them by clicking on "OK".

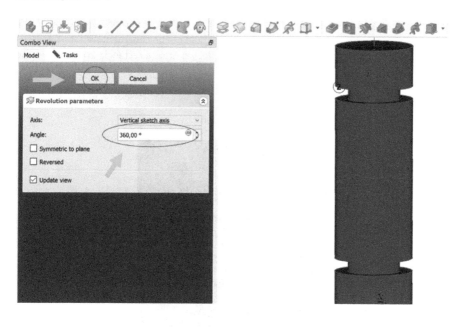

The tools "Subtractive Loft" and "Subtractive Pipe":

These two tools work in the same way as their additive counterparts ("Additive Loft" and "Additive Pipe"), only in a subtractive way. Think back for a moment and consider what we might need for the two tools.

For "Subtractive Loft" we need two sketches on different planes. In this case, these planes can be, for example, the upper and lower surfaces of a simple body. We create a cube with an edge length of 50 mm each so that we have an object from which we can remove material.

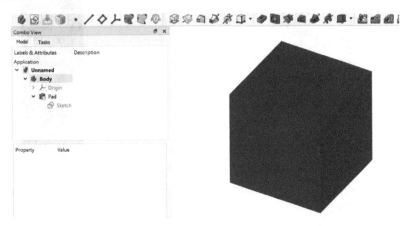

Then we need two sketches. We draw one sketch on the upper and one on the lower side of the cube, as already announced. The sketches should not be congruent. We start with the sketch for the upper face of the cube. For example, we draw a rectangle 20 mm wide and 15 mm high.

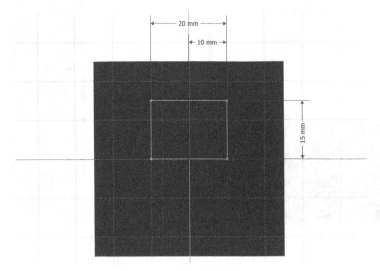

After the sketch is completely defined, we can close it. Then we start a new sketch on the lower face of the cube. For example, we draw a rectangle 20 mm wide and 10 mm high. We also define this sketch completely and then close it.

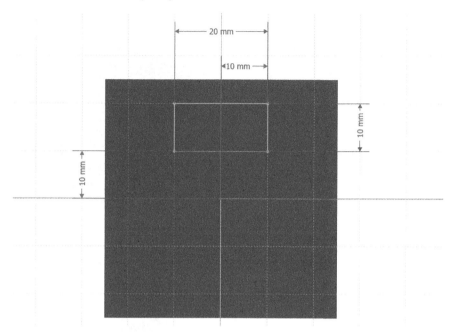

Now we can execute the command "Subtractive Loft" by selecting the two sketches in the part browser (CTRL key pressed).

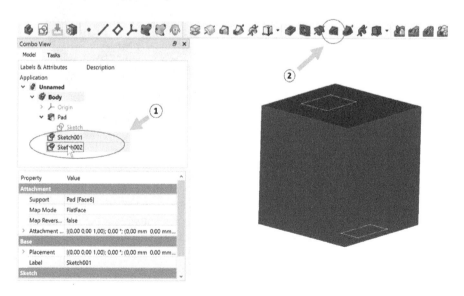

Unfortunately, a preview is not shown to us in this case, but we can simply click on "OK" and then see the desired result. The two surfaces have been connected with a cutout.

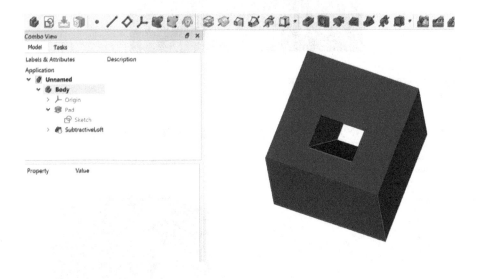

For the command "Subtractive Pipe" we need two sketches and a path. For example, we could draw a circle of any diameter on each of the top and bottom sides of the cube. You can probably do this on your own by now. Where you place the circles is not relevant for this example.

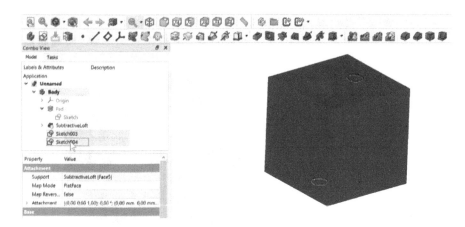

Afterwards, we still need a path, which we sketch, for example, on the y-z plane. For a better representation, we hide the cube for the sketch by clicking on the body in the part browser and using the space bar. For example, the path could be a diagonal line running from the top face to the bottom face. We then close the sketch.

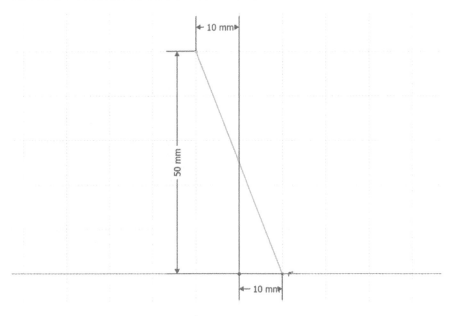

After that - just like with the function "Additive Pipe" - we first select the sketch and then the command "Subtractive Pipe".

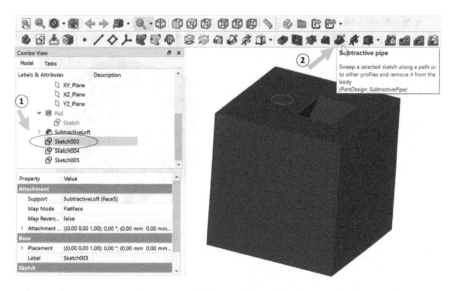

In the combo view, we can then press the button "Object" in the area "Path" and then select the path in the cube. The program will then generate the preview of the function.

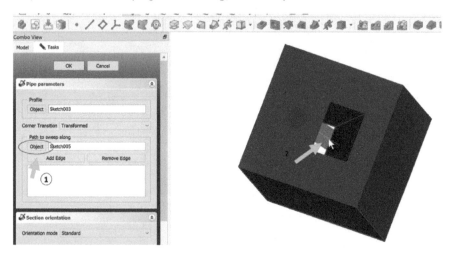

We still confirm with "OK" and the subtractive command is implemented.

If we move the PC mouse over the created elements in the part browser, we can better see the result of the two tools, "Subtractive Loft" and "Subtractive Pipe".

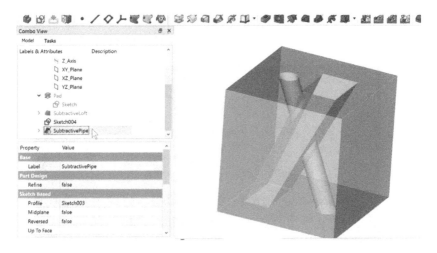

Excellent! Now you know the most important subtractive commands. It's nice that we've come this far. We'll now look at a few more tools before moving on to the design projects. Stay tuned, it will be worth it!

3.4.3 Tools for mirroring and pattern creation

The following two tools are very useful if you want to reduce the time and effort of designing. With the functions "Mirrored" and "Linear Pattern" you can mirror geometries and create patterns.

The tool "Mirrored":

You can use this tool if you want to duplicate one or more objects of a component by mirroring them on a plane. Let's take a closer look. For example, we will create a cuboid with a base of 30 mm x 60 mm and a height of 10 mm.

The object we would like to mirror should be a simple hole. For this hole, we will create a sketch on the upper surface of the box. For example, the hole should have a diameter of 6 mm and be positioned 22 mm or 7 mm from the origin.

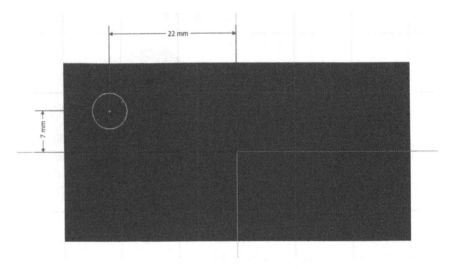

After the sketch is completed, we create the hole using the "Hole" command.

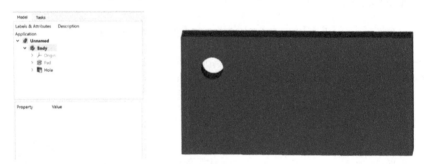

For the command "Mirrored" we now first select the hole in the part browser and then click on the command in the toolbar. The program then creates a preview of the mirrored object for us.

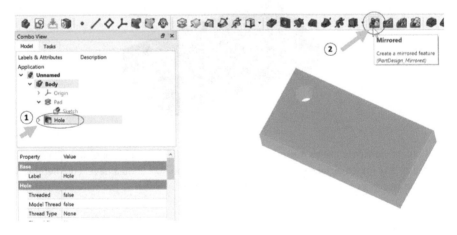

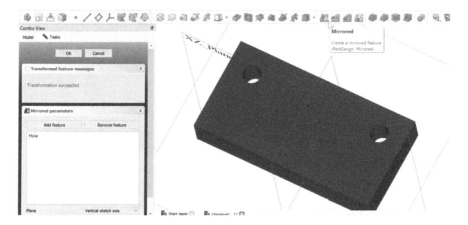

As we can see, the hole has been mirrored using the y-z plane. If we need a mirroring based on another plane - e.g. the x-z plane - we can do it in the combo view at the setting "Plane".

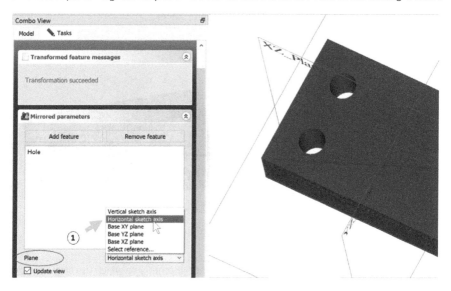

If we want to mirror several objects - e.g. two or three holes - we simply select them by holding down the CTRL key before starting the "Mirrored" command. We can also select the command "Mirrored" first and then add all the desired objects with "Add feature" (combo view).

The tool "Linear Pattern":

With this tool, we can create a linear pattern, that is, we can duplicate objects with a defined distance. Let's see how this works. We will apply this function to the cuboid we have just created. To do this, delete the mirrored hole by selecting it in the part browser and pressing the Remove button.

Then we select the first hole in the part browser and click on the command "Linear Pattern".

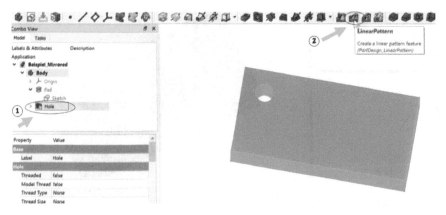

Now we have to fill the settings "Direction", "Length" and "Occurrences", which are located in the lower part of the combo view, with meaningful values.

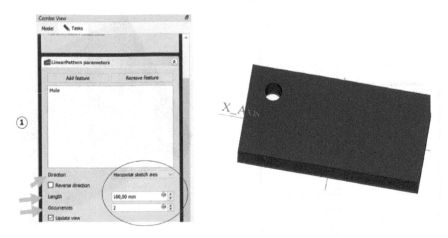

With the setting "Direction" you select the reference geometry to which the linear pattern is oriented. For example, if we choose the x-axis here, the pattern will be created along this axis.

At "Length" we enter the distance that should exist between the individual holes of the pattern, e.g., 43 mm. And at "Occurrences" we enter the number of holes we want, e.g., four. By the way, if "Update view" is checked, the changes will be shown to us live as a preview. This is an excellent help when selecting the distance and the number.

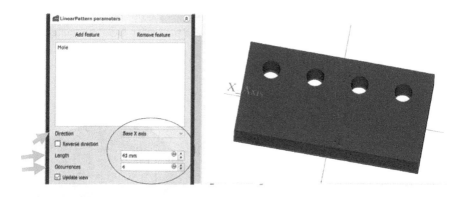

Similar to the "Mirrored" tool, we can also change the direction of the pattern here. To do this, simply specify a different axis, e.g., the y-axis, at "Direction". Of course, you must then also change the distance between the holes and the number of holes.

3.4.4 Tools for advanced 3D modeling

For the last three important tools from the "Part Design" workspace, we again create a cube whose edge lengths are 50 mm each.

The tool "Fillet":

You may remember the function "Fillet" from the 2D area. Just like in a 2D sketch, you can also fillet edges on the 3D object. To accomplish this, we simply select the desired edge, or several desired edges. For example, we select all the edges of the upper face of the cube (holding down the CTRL key for multiple selection) and then click on the command "Fillet" in the toolbar.

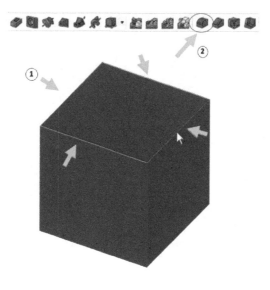

In the combo view, you can then set the desired fillet radius in the lower area, e.g., 5 mm. In the upper area, you can also add further edges with the button "Add" if required. With "OK" the fillets are created.

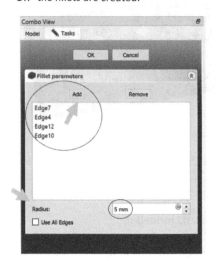 

The tool "Chamfer":

With this tool, you can bevel an edge instead of rounding it. But that is the only difference between this tool and the "Fillet" tool. The procedure is identical. Select the desired edge, e.g., an edge of the lower face of the cube, and then click on the command "Chamfer" in the toolbar.

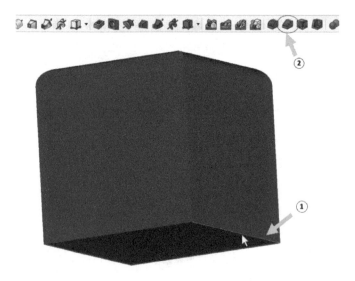

In the combo view, you can then make the desired settings.

The tool "Thickness":

This tool is ideal if you want to create a hollowed 3D body quickly. In other CAD programs, this command is often referred to as "Shell" or Wall.

We first delete the two features "Fillet" and "Chamfer" so that we have our cube as the initial object again. Alternatively, we can simply create a new one.

To execute the command, we then first click on the face of the cube and then select the tool "Thickness" from the toolbar.

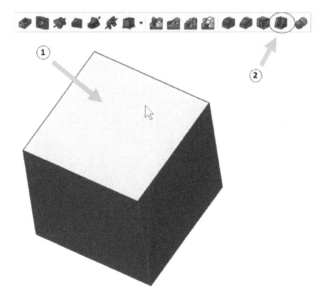

Afterwards, we are shown a preview. In the combo view we can make the desired settings, we change the option "Thickness" e.g., to 5 mm and select in the option "Mode" the setting "Skin". In addition, we select the setting "Intersection" at "Join Type".

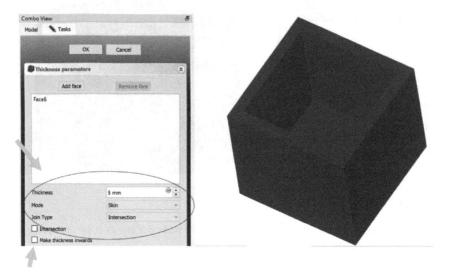

By the way: If you activate the option "Make thickness inwards" - to be found in the lower area - the wall will not be added to the outside but to the inside. Try it and you will see the difference.

4 Design projects

4.1 First project: mounting component

The first design object is a simple fastening component. It can be fastened using two bolts and is used, for example, to hold an axle. The following illustration shows the final 3D model from different perspectives. You can see the front of the part (top left), the top view (bottom left), the side view (top right) and the isometric view (bottom right).

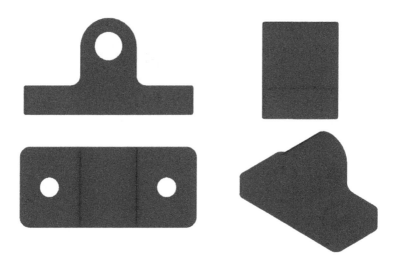

To do this, we start a new document and switch to the "Part Design" workspace, just as we learned. Then - after we have created a body with "Body" - we start a sketch on one of the three planes. For example, we choose the x-z plane. Why the x-z plane? Because on this plane, we will draw the front side of the object as a 2D sketch, so that the "Front" view of the program will also correspond to this front side.

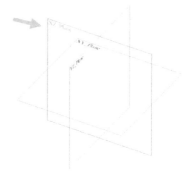

We now simply draw as a 2D sketch the geometry that we see when we look at the object from the front. We can then extrude this later in three dimensions. Let´s build up the 2D geometry block by block.

First, we draw a rectangle ("Centered Rectangle") with a width of 90 mm and a height of 15 mm, the center of which should be at the coordinate origin. You can also add the dimensions here ("Constrain vertical distance" and "Constrain horizontal distance"). Then we remove the upper line of the rectangle because we don't need it. Alternatively, we could have just drawn three single lines.

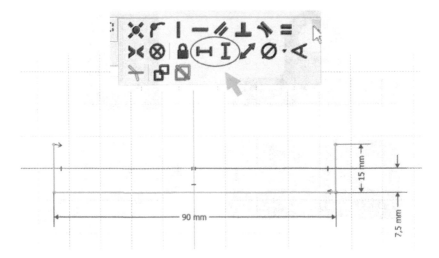

Then we add two more horizontal and two more vertical lines. We dimension the horizontal lines with 30 mm and the vertical lines with 20 mm.

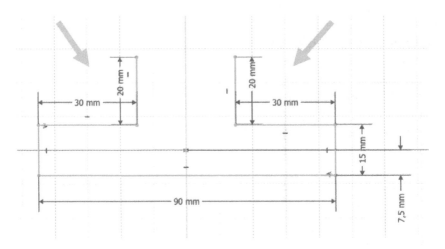

The last segment of the base consists of a semicircle. For this, we select an arc with the command "End points and rim point". We select both corner points of the vertical lines one after the other and finally any point in the upper area so that the arc is created. Then we assign a diameter of 30 mm to the circle with "Constrain arc or circle".

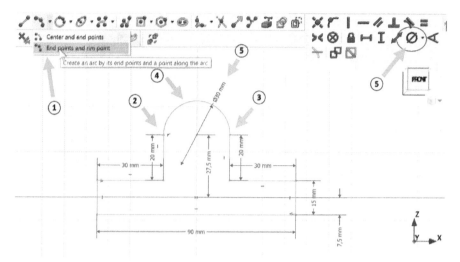

In order for the sketch to be completely defined, we must also dimension the distance from the center of the arc to the coordinate origin. The distance must be 27.5 mm, which can be calculated using the existing dimensions.

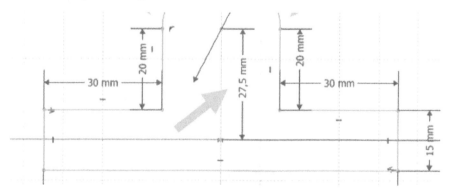

Note: For a three-dimensional extrusion, you always need a single and contiguous surface as a 2D sketch. This is what we have created here. We could also have built the sketch from two rectangles and a semicircle - think of building blocks - but then we would have two lines dividing the surface into three segments.

Now we can close the sketch and create the 3D part using the function "Pad". We need a dimension of e.g., 40 mm. With the setting "Type" we can leave "Dimension", then the component will be extruded to the front. The x-z plane is then on the back of the component.

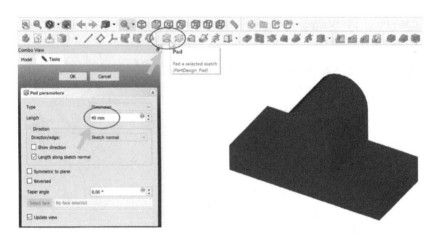

Alternatively, we could select the option "Two dimensions" and enter 20 mm per side, then the x-z plane would be exactly in the middle of the component.

In the next step, we still create the hole in the upper part of the component. To do this, we need to start a new 2D sketch on the front - or back - side of the part. Then create a circle with a diameter of 15 mm, whose center should be on the z-axis (vertical line). To complete the definition, we then need a dimension in the z-direction, e.g., 28 mm from the center of the circle to the coordinate origin.

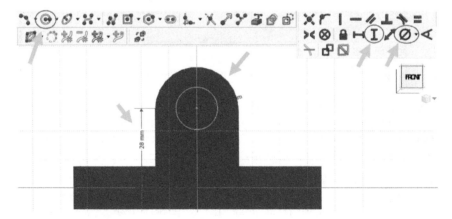

You may notice now that we could have integrated this step right into the first 2D sketch. That is indeed correct and would have saved us some time.

After we have closed the sketch, we can now execute the hole either with the command "Pocket" or also with the command "Hole". In this case, both functions do the same thing. If we decide to use the command "Hole", we have to enter the diameter of 15 mm in the setting "Diameter" and in the setting "Depth" we have to choose the option "Through all".

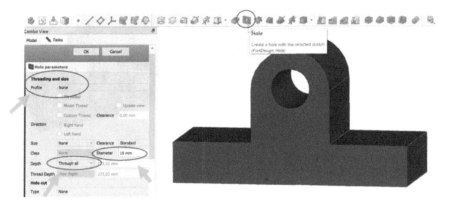

For the two mounting holes, we start a sketch on the underside of the object. Here we draw two circles, each with a diameter of 10 mm, whose centers should lie on the (horizontal) x-axis. In addition, we dimension these two circles with a distance of 30 mm each to the coordinate origin.

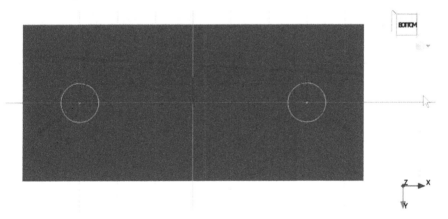

After closing the sketch, we once again use the command "Hole". We have to select the options as shown.

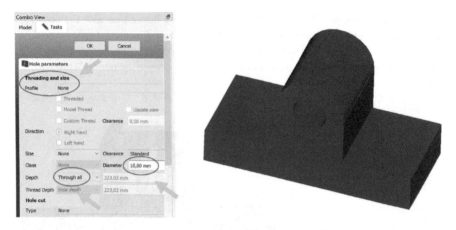

Meanwhile, our first 3D object is as good as finished. We can finish off by rounding off a few edges using the "Fillet" function. You are welcome to do this independently, according to your wishes.

For example, we could round each of the following edges with 5 mm.

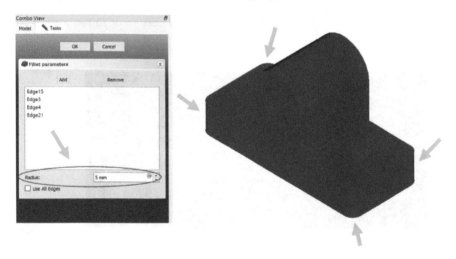

In addition, we can round all the other edges by 1 mm each. We do this by clicking on the front face of the part, selecting the command "Fillet" and then activating the option "Select all Edges".

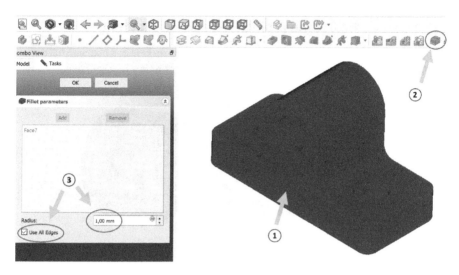

If we now take a final look at the part browser, we will find all the sketches and commands that we needed or created for this object. With a right click (or double click) on it and the selection of "Edit" we can edit each element again. For a better overview we can also change the designations, this makes sense especially for more complex constructions.

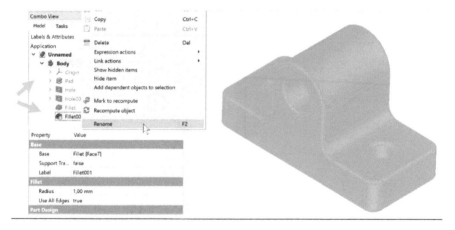

Important: Please be sure to save the part, as we will need it again later. To do this, simply click on "Save as ..." in the menu bar at "File".

4.2 Second project: Hexagon socket bolt

In this second design project, we want to design an M8 x 30 socket head bolt with full thread length. We can find the dimensions for this on the Internet or in a mechanical engineering table book or a standard parts catalog.

We can design this bolt in two ways. Firstly, with the help of one or more extrusions, and secondly, as a turned part with the help of the function "Revolution". We will take the latter way because it leads faster to the goal. To do this, we first need one half of the cross-section of the bolt. You can imagine that you cut the bolt in the middle. We need to draw one half of the profile, which can then be seen. For this, we first create a new document, create a body and then create a sketch on the x-z plane.

On this plane, we draw a 3.23 mm long horizontal line whose starting point should be on the coordinate origin. We connect a 30 mm long vertical line to it.

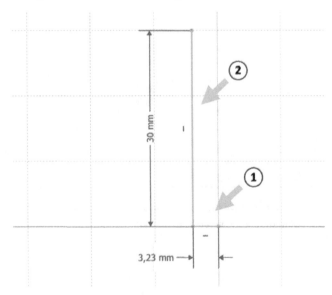

For the head we need a 3.267 mm horizontal line, an 8 mm vertical line and another 6.5 mm horizontal line. Finally, we connect the top point with the bottom point using a vertical line so that the profile is completely closed.

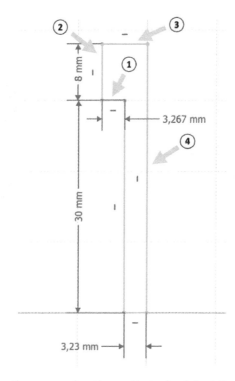

As you can see from the green color, the profile is also fully defined. Please always pay attention to this. This profile is now half of the cross-section of the bolt. After we have finished the sketch, we can rotate the profile around an axis in 3D mode and thus create the basic body.

To do this, we make sure that the sketch is selected in the part browser and then click on the "Revolution" function.

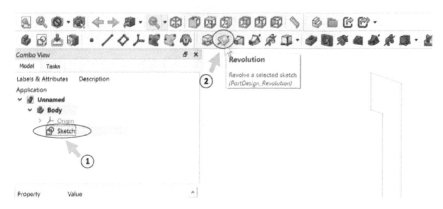

The program automatically selects the rotation axis and creates a preview of the 3D object for us.

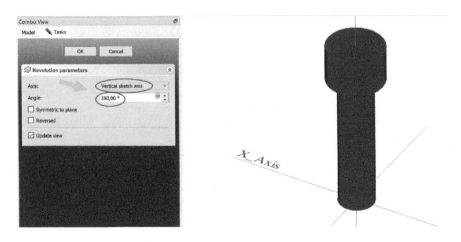

This looks good! As rotation axis, we can leave "Vertical sketch axis". Alternatively, we could select the z-axis.

In the meantime, the basic body of the bolt has been created. The thread is still missing.

Before creating the thread, we first add fillets. We round the edges of the head by 0.5 mm each. To do this, we simply select the upper and lower surfaces of the head (hold down the CTRL key for multiple selection) and then click on the function "Fillet".

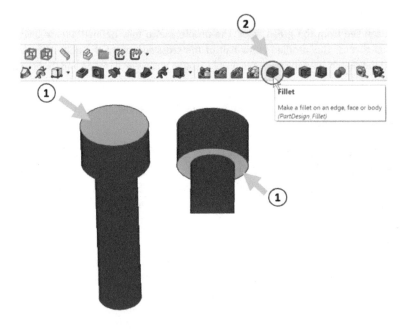

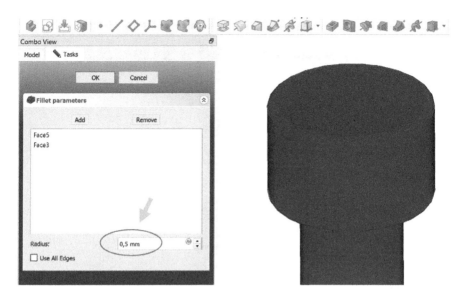

In the next step, we dedicate ourselves to the thread. So that we do not have to draw the thread profile ourselves, we install an add-on called "ThreadProfile". To install it, we have to go to the menu "Tools" and click on "Addon Manager". We can confirm the next window with "OK".

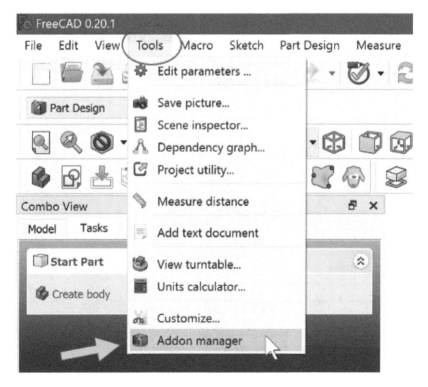

We are then in the "Addon Manager", in which we search for "ThreadProfile".

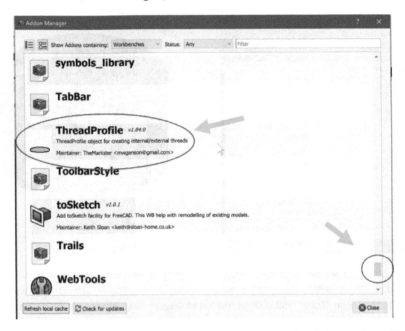

After clicking on the add-on, we can install it in the next window by clicking on "Install".

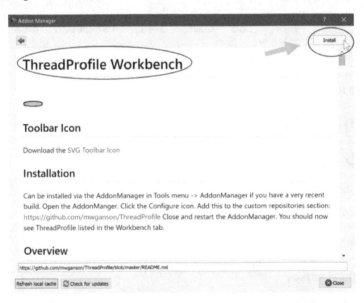

After that, we can close the "Addon Manager" again. We can find the installed add-on in the drop-down menu of the workspaces. We select "ThreadProfile".

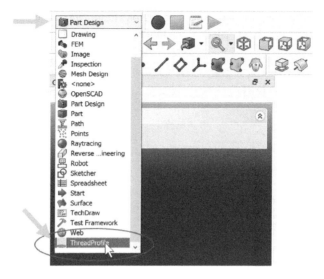

Then the functions of the add-on appear in the toolbar. To create the thread, we first select the command "Create V thread profile".

In the lower area of the combo view, the setting options appear. Here we can select the desired thread at the setting "Presets", e.g., a normal M8 thread with a pitch of 1.25 ("M8 coarse 1.25"). Make sure that you do <u>not</u> select a fine thread (we need "coarse" instead of "fine").

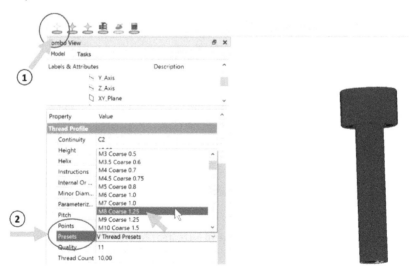

All the required values have now been added automatically by this add-on. The only value we still have to change is the length of the thread. We do this at the setting "Height". We need 30 mm.

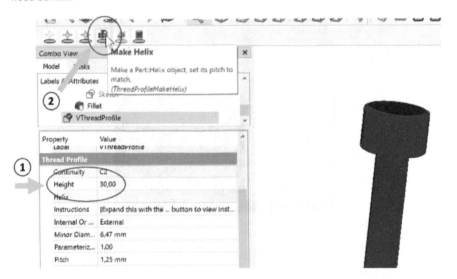

Now we can create the thread by clicking on "Make Helix" first to create the spiral path for the thread.

Then we select the profile "VThreadProfile" and the spiral "Helix" in the part browser (CTRL key) and then click on "Do Sweep".

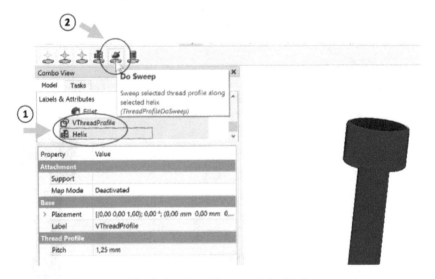

Then it takes a little time and finally the thread is created. Perfect!

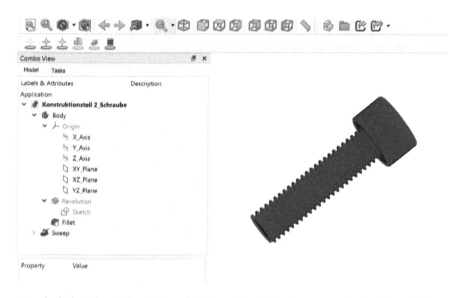

Now the bolt is almost done! The only thing missing is the hexagon socket profile, which we need to hold the tool. For this, we must first switch back to the workspace "Part Design".

Then we create a hole on the top surface of the bolt head by selecting the top surface and the command "Hole". We do not need to make a 2D sketch in this case, because the hole should be exactly centered. The program can do this automatically.

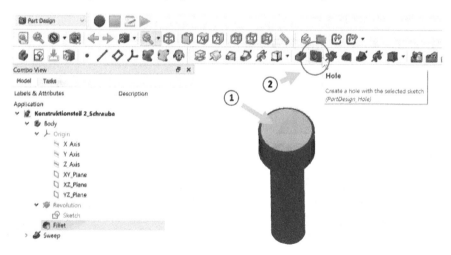

The hole should be 4 mm deep and have a diameter of 6 mm. After we have entered these values in the settings, we still confirm with "OK".

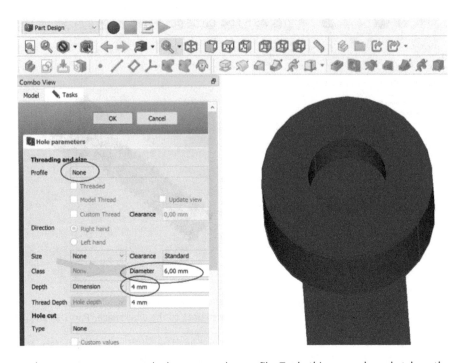

In the next step, we create the hexagon socket profile. To do this, we make a sketch on the top surface of the bolt head. For the profile, we draw a polygon. We need six sides because we want to draw a hexagon.

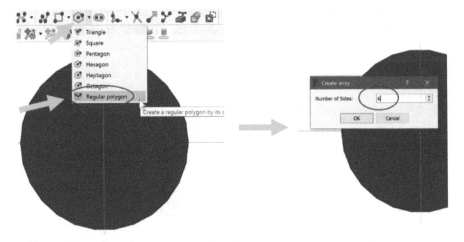

We set the center of the polygon to the coordinate origin. After that, we need to click once more in the plane and the polygon will be created.

In the next step, we dimension the outer circle of the polygon with a diameter of 6.93 mm and set a corner point of the hexagon to the horizontal x-axis with the command "Constrain point onto object". Then the profile is completely defined, and we can close the sketch.

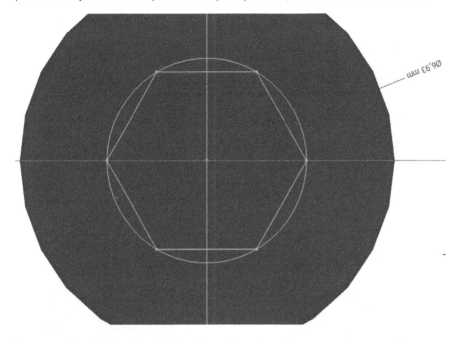

Then we select the function "Pocket" from the subtractive commands area and create a cutout of 4 mm length.

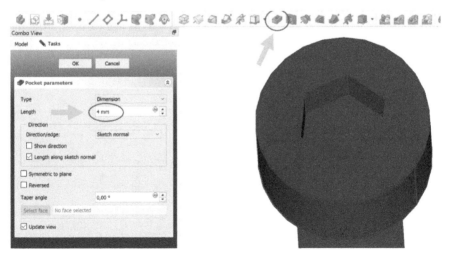

Perfectly done! Now the hexagon socket bolt is ready! **Be sure to save it, as we will need the part again later.** Great that you've made it this far already. We'll move on to the next project right away.

4.3 Third project: mug with handle

In this chapter, we want to construct a cup including the handle. We will first construct the basic shape, i.e., the cup without the handle, and then add the handle.

First we start - in a new document - a sketch on the x-y plane and create a circle. The diameter of the circle could be e.g., 90 mm, the center should be on the origin of the coordinate system so that the sketch is fully defined.

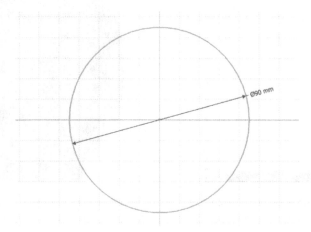

After closing the sketch, we can create a cylinder with a dimension of 80 mm from the sketch using the function "Pad".

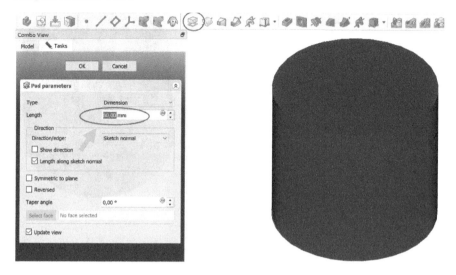

To create a cup from the cylinder, we use the function "Thickness". To do this, we first click on the upper surface of the cylinder and then on the function in the toolbar.

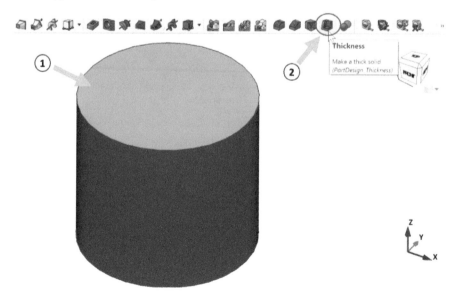

In the settings in the combo view, we determine the wall thickness, e.g., 5 mm. In addition, we change the setting "Join Type" to the option "Intersection" and activate the option "Make thickness inwards" so that the diameter of our cup is not changed. If we did not enable this option, the wall would be added to the outside and the cup would become larger. However, we do not want that.

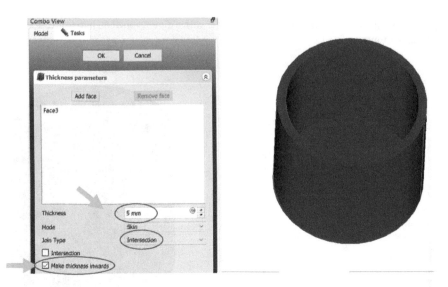

By the way, in the Part browser (combo view and tab "Model") we can see the construction progress with the individual features. As we can see here, we have created a sketch for the "Pad" command and then applied the command. Therefore, the program has automatically moved the sketch to the "Pad" command. This is followed by the "Thickness" command. When we select a feature in the part browser, we can edit, rename or delete it.

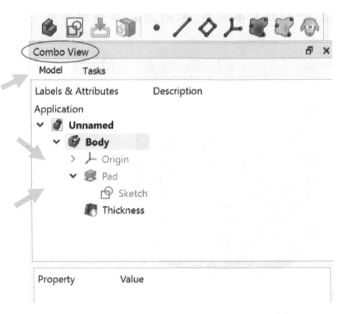

So now we have the basic shape of the cup. For the handle, we first need a parallel plane to the edge of the cup so that the handle sits slightly lower than the edge of the cup. We create a new plane with the command "Create Datum Plane" from the toolbar.

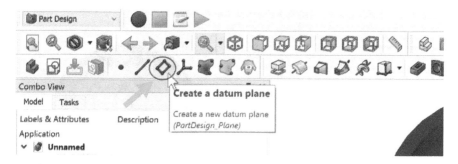

We click on the command and then have to select a reference for the new plane. In our case, this reference is the top edge of the cup, since we want to create a plane parallel to this surface.

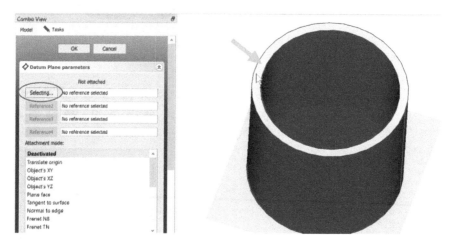

In the lower area in the settings in the combo view, we can then enter the desired offset.

We need -15 mm in z-direction because we intend to create the plane 15 mm below the edge of the cup.

We have to move in negative z-axis direction for this, hence the minus sign. Furthermore, we then confirm with "OK" and find the parallel plane in the part browser.

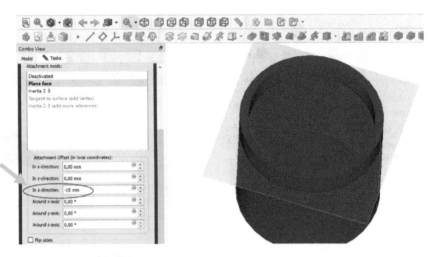

Then create a sketch on this layer by selecting the layer in the Part browser and clicking the "Create Sketch" command as usual.

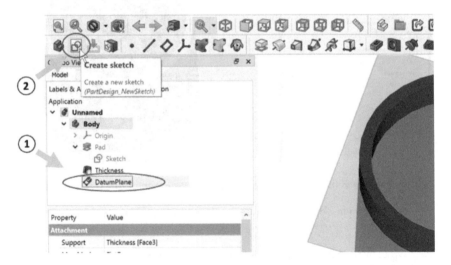

On this layer, we now draw the sketch of our handle. For this, we need a rectangle, which we draw to the right of the cup.

The rectangle should measure 20 mm x 30 mm and sit centered on the x-axis, so we dimension one of the top or bottom corners of the rectangle 10 mm from the coordinate origin.

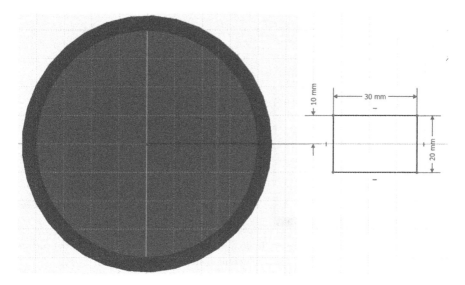

For the correct placement of the handle in x-direction, we finally add a 43.5 mm dimension between the rectangle and the coordinate origin. We need this dimension so that the rectangle sits a small distance inside the cup. This is necessary because otherwise the edges of the handle will not merge with the edge of the cup. In this case, the element is added to the basic cylindrical element, i.e., the cup, in an additive manner.

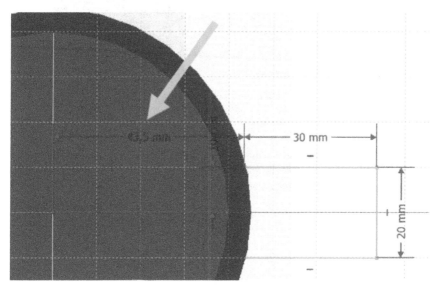

Now we can close the sketch and then extrude the handle using the "Pad" function. It is important that we activate the option "Reversed" in the settings so that the handle is extruded downwards (negative z-axis direction). The dimension can be, for example, 50 mm.

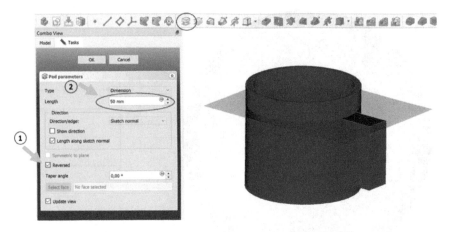

We now require another handle hole. To do this, we start a new sketch on the front surface of the handle. Click on the surface and select the command "Create sketch".

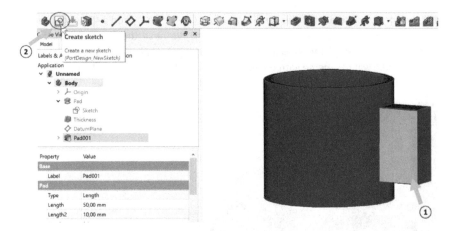

Here, draw a 20 mm wide and 40 mm high rectangle from a center point ("Centered Rectangle") to the right of the handle and add a dimension of 40 mm from the center of the rectangle to the coordinate origin to define the vertical position of the rectangle.

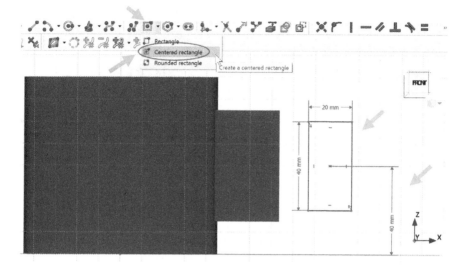

We then add a dimension of 59 mm in the horizontal direction to obtain the correct position of the rectangle in the x-direction.

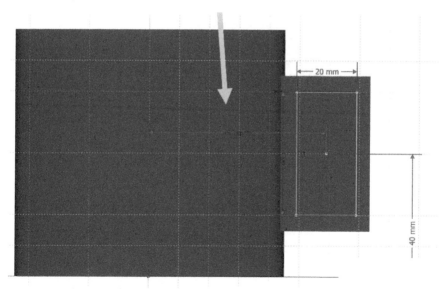

By the way: If you ever don't know why a sketch is not yet completely defined (green color), you can also simply drag the sketched geometry once to see in which direction movements are still possible.

We can then close the sketch. Then, using the "Pocket" function, we can make a cutout in 3D mode. For a section that goes completely through the material, we select the option "Through all" in the combo view for the "Type" setting.

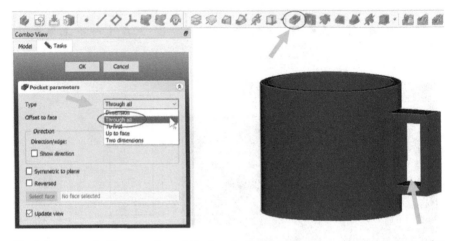

Finally, we round off some edges of the handle and the cup. You are welcome to try this once, completely according to your own ideas. Basically, it only serves the design here and is a matter of taste. You can also select a surface instead of individual edges, the program will then take all edges of this surface into account.

As a last design project, we will design a screwdriver. Afterwards, we will deal with further work areas and functions of the software "FreeCAD". Among other things, we will learn how to assemble individual 3D models virtually into an assembly and how to create engineering drawings. Keep at it, and please continue, it will be worth it!

4.4 Fourth project: Screwdriver

We will construct a slotted screwdriver with handle in this section. The construction will succeed most easily if we start with the handle of the screwdriver and create it as a rotational part.

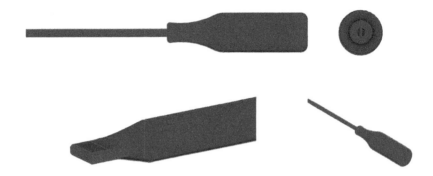

As with any 3D model, we first create a 2D sketch again, e.g., on the x-z plane and draw half of the cross-section of the handle. For this, we need, for example, a 110 mm long and horizontal line, which we dimension with 55 mm distance between an end point of the line and the coordinate origin.

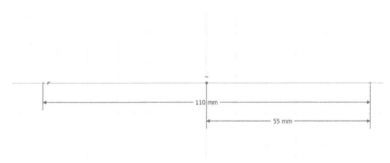

We also draw a 15 mm long and vertical line and a 70 mm long and horizontal line following it. These lines represent the first part of the handle for the screwdriver.

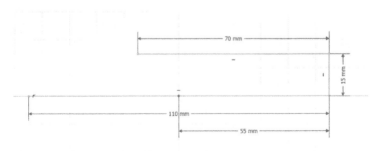

For the second part of the handle, we need an 8 mm long and vertical line and a 3-point arc connecting the previous profile. For the arc, it is best to choose the command "End points and rim point". Then click first on the end point of the vertical line, then on the end point of the horizontal line, and finally again in the drawing area in between. Then add the diameter. The arc should have a diameter of, for example, 120 mm.

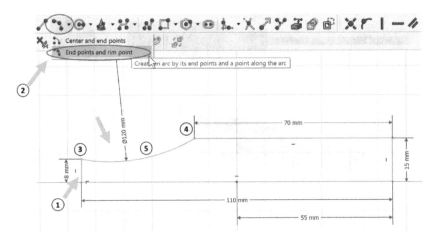

Now the profile for the rotation is ready. The profile represents half of the cross-section of the handle. We will not draw the blade and the blade tip or bit in this 2D sketch. If you like, you can add the blade tip (half of the cross-section) to this sketch as well, but we will add it as an extrusion right away. We can therefore close the sketch.

Using the function "Revolute" we can create the profile with a 360-degree rotation around the x-axis.

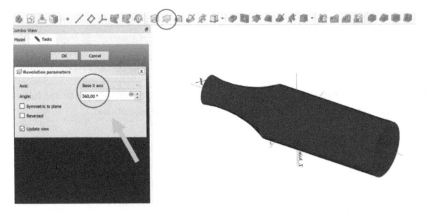

If an error appears, you must select the option "Base X axis" in the combo view at the setting "Axis".

To further refine the model of the handle, we can make fillets using the "Fillet" command. For example, we could choose a radius of 5 mm for the rear outer edge of the screwdriver handle and 15 mm and 2 mm for the transitions in the front area. Use the command here for each edge, i.e., three times in total.

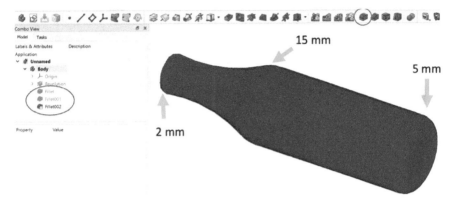

As already mentioned, we will now add the blade of the screwdriver, this we will sketch on the front surface of the handle. We will create a sketch for this purpose.

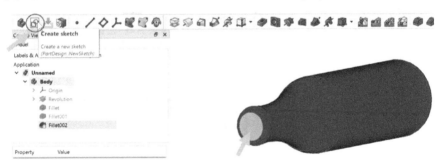

For the later linear extrusion, we now only need a circle whose center lies congruently on the coordinate origin. The diameter should be e.g., 6 mm.

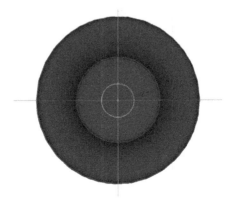

Then we extrude the profile by 100 mm (command "Pad") and in this way we get the screwdriver blade.

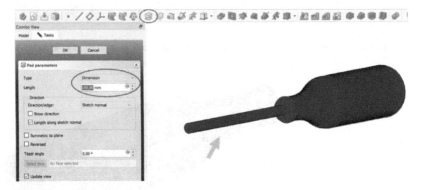

Now the bit or the blade tip in the front area is still missing. We want to construct a slotted screwdriver, so we will use the "Additive Loft" command further on to create the bit. What do we need for this? That's right, a parallel plane and a sketch. We first create the plane that will be parallel to the face of the tip by using the command "Create a datum plane".

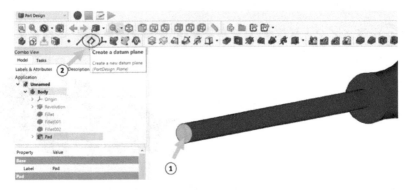

We need a distance of 8 mm in the z-direction.

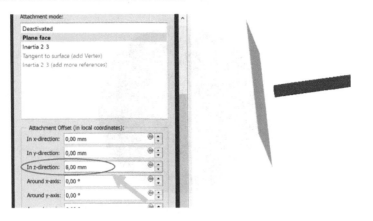

On this plane, we can now draw the rectangular profile of the bit. For this, we use a rectangle whose center lies on the coordinate origin. We also dimension the rectangle with a length of 5.8 mm and a width of 1.5 mm.

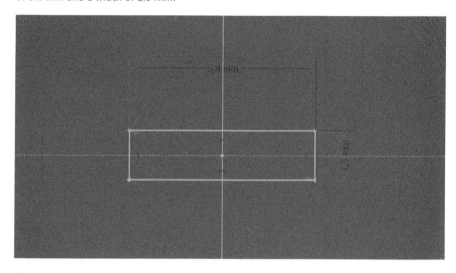

After we have closed the 2D sketch and hidden the plane for a better view of the profile (select the plane in the part browser and press the space bar), we can use the "Additive Loft" command to connect the sketched profile with the circular geometry of the screwdriver blade. To do this, we select the sketch in the part browser and then click on the face of the screwdriver blade while holding down the CTRL key. Meanwhile, we can select the command "Additive Loft" and the program will generate the 3D preview. We can confirm with "OK".

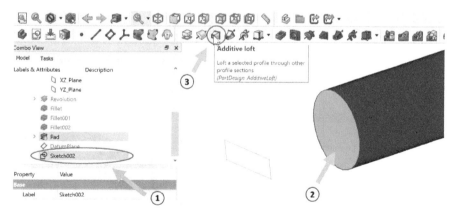

This gives us a nice transition between the blade and the bit.

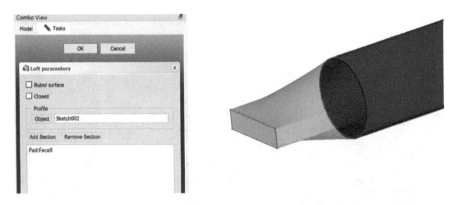

Since the rectangular shape of the bit is now a bit too small at the front to be able to bolt with it, we now have to extend it a bit. We don't even have to create a sketch for this, but can simply click on the surface and the command "Pad". The program will then automatically know that we want to use the sketch geometry of this face for the extrusion. We only change the length of the extrusion to 3 mm.

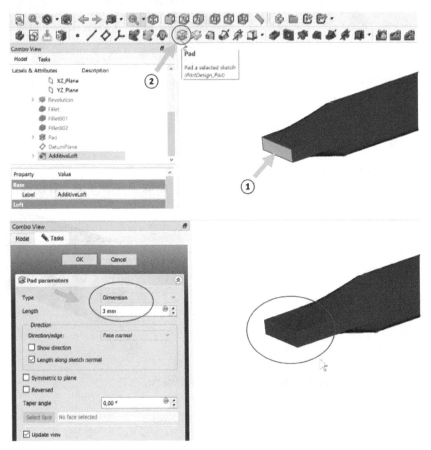

Now it looks better. Finally, we add a 0.3 mm chamfer to each of the horizontal edges of the bit using the "Chamfer" command. An error message may appear because the preselected 1 mm chamfer would not be possible. You can simply click away the error message after entering the 0.3 mm value.

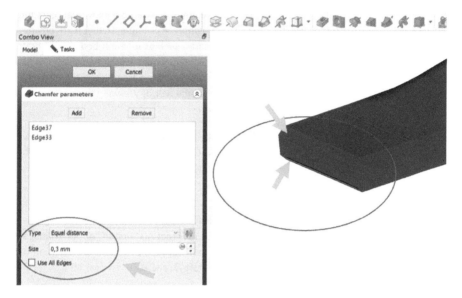

Perfect! Now we've constructed some great 3D objects. That wasn't so hard, was it?

In the following chapters, we will deal with the assembly of individual parts in "FreeCAD", as well as the creation of technical drawings. Soon we will have done it! You are welcome to try your hand at a few constructions of your own in advance - for practice purposes.

5 Other Workspaces in "FreeCAD"

5.1 The "Assembly (A2 Plus)" Workspace

In most CAD programs, there is a workspace where you can assemble individual parts into an assembly. This is also the case in "FreeCAD". Imagine, for example, that you are buying a piece of furniture. It consists of many individual parts, such as wooden boards and bolts, and usually has to be assembled when it is delivered. You would also design the individual wooden boards and bolts in CAD as independent parts and then assemble them - virtually, so to speak. This works schematically similar to the real world. We will take a look at the procedure in this chapter.

Why go to all this trouble? Virtual assembly plays an important role in the design of parts. It helps to check whether the designed individual parts can be assembled into an assembly without problems or collisions.

Installation:

The "Assembly2Plus (A2plus)" workspace is not installed by default when the program is installed. Therefore, we have to add this workspace in "FreeCAD" first in "Addon Manager" (tab "Tools"). We had used this one before. Look for "A2plus", click on it and then on the button "Install". Thereafter, we must be sure to restart "FreeCAD".

A2plus

We will then find the "A2plus Workbench" in the drop-down menu of the workspaces.

To learn how to assemble individual components, we would like to use our first design project (fastening component) and our second project (bolt). We will also create a baseplate on which we will mount the components and a shaft that we want to insert between two mounting components. This is what it will look like in the end.

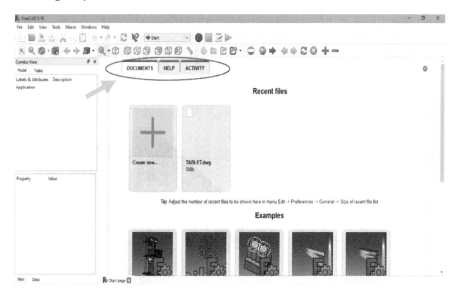

To do this, we must first construct two new parts. Please construct independently a rectangular mounting plate consisting of a rectangular sketch (length: 200 mm and width: 120 mm), edge fillets (e.g., 10 mm for the four vertical edges and 2 mm for all other edges) and 4 holes. For the holes, you can first create the following sketch.

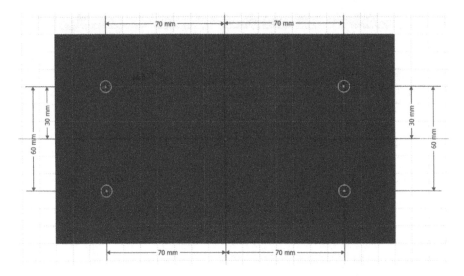

Then use the command "Hole" and select a M8 threaded hole with 20 mm depth. Important: We do not activate the option "Model Thread" here because otherwise we would get problems during assembly.

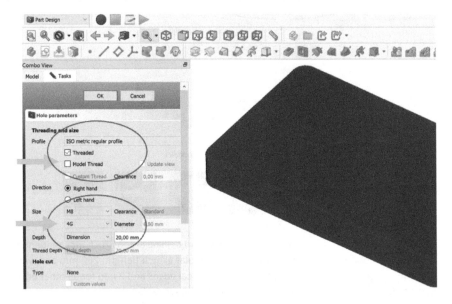

In addition, we still need a shaft, which is simply a cylindrical element with a diameter of 14.5 mm and a length of 180 mm. You can certainly construct this independently by now. After we have saved both parts, we can deal with the workspace "A2plus" and the assembly.

To assemble our components, we first create a new document and then switch to the "A2plus" workspace. This document will become our assembly. The first thing we do is save this document.

The next step is to import our parts into the assembly. We do this with the command "Add a part from an external file", which we find in the top left of the menu bar. We click on it, navigate to the directory where our parts are stored and select the mounting plate as the first part.

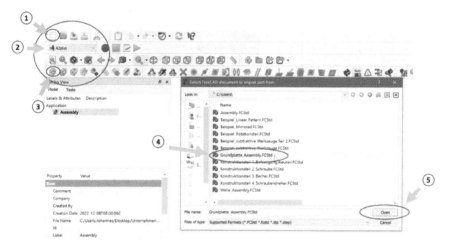

The first part that is inserted into an assembly is always automatically fixed in 3D space by the program, all subsequent parts are freely movable and must be assembled virtually. Therefore, you always select as the first part the part that would also be the basic part in the real world, i.e. the part on which the entire assembly is based or with which the assembly process begins.

We then use the identical procedure to add the mounting component. After we have selected the part, we can place it in the workspace with one click. It does not matter where we place the part for now.

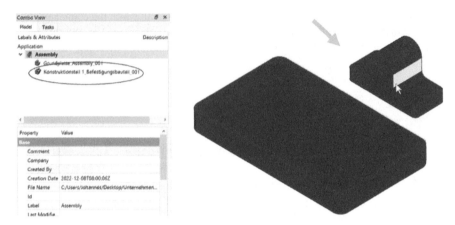

Using the command "Move the selected part under constraints" we can move the part freely in 3D space. Using the command "Move" we can move the part along the coordinate axes and rotate it around these axes.

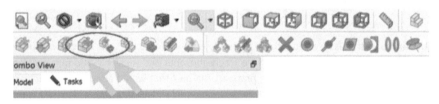

In fact, the part does not yet have any constraints and can therefore be moved completely freely.

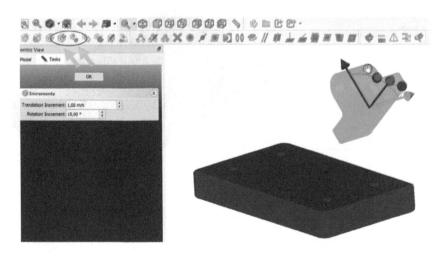

We will change this during the assembly process. Our task is to fix the part in its final position using constraints. In the broadest sense, this process is similar to the use of the constraints in a 2D sketch.

For the assembly, we have many constraints available for this in the middle area of the toolbar. These are currently gray and not selectable.

The first step of our assembly is now to place the mounting component on the base plate. We do this by selecting the lower surface of the mounting component and the upper surface of the base plate (CTRL key pressed). After that, the constraints that make sense in this case will be visible. We want to make the two surfaces coincident, so we select the command "Add planeCoincident constraint".

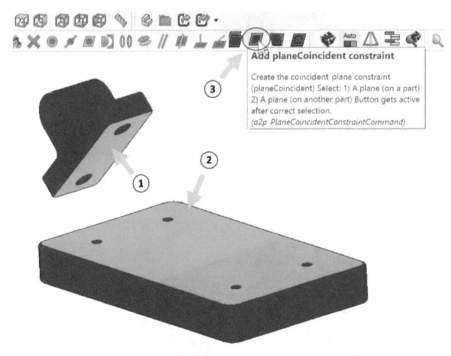

The part is then placed on the base plate and a window appears where you can set the properties of the link. When you are satisfied with the alignment, simply click on the button "Accept".

However, you can still change the orientation here by clicking the "Flip direction" button.

The surfaces are now still congruent, but the part has simply been turned over. You can also enter an offset if the part has to be mounted at a certain distance from the baseplate. However, we do not need that here.

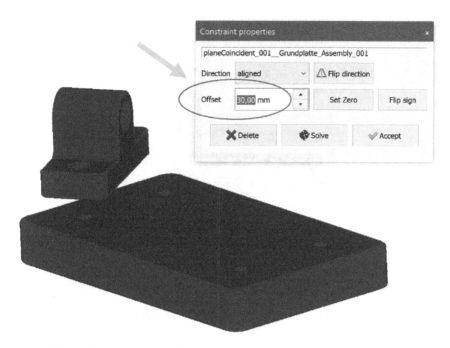

After clicking the button "Accept" we can try to move the part with the command "Move the selected parts under constraints". We notice that we can move the part, but it always stays on the surface where we just fixed it. So, we have created the first constraint. This is also shown to us in the part browser at the two parts, and can be changed or deleted here.

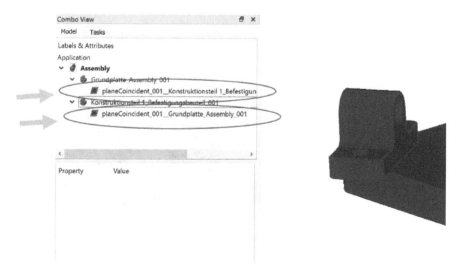

We now want to align our fastening component using the holes so that we can then fasten it with two bolts. We do this by selecting a hole in the mounting component and the correctly positioned hole in the baseplate (CTRL key pressed).

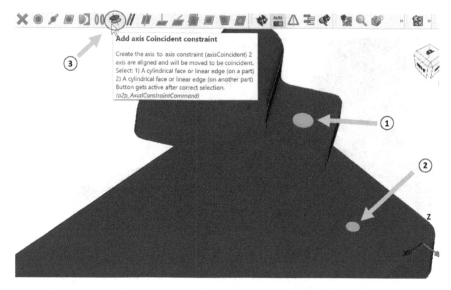

Only two constraints are possible for this combination. We want the axes of the holes to be coincident, and therefore we choose the command "Add axis Coincident constraint".

The holes are aligned with each other by moving the mounting part to the hole of the baseplate. In addition, the window with the settings for the constraint appears again. If everything fits, we can click on the button "Accept".

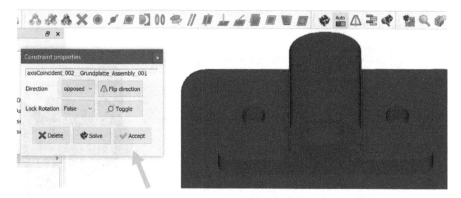

Now we can no longer move the part, we could only turn it. In order to achieve the correct position, we also make the other two holes congruent. This works in an identical way.

If the dimensions are correct, no error will appear, if the holes have different distances, an error message will appear, and we would thereby be able to recognize that we have constructed incorrectly. The first fastening part is now correctly placed. We now need to add two more bolts.

Inserting the bolt works the same way as inserting the other two parts. After placing a bolt in the workspace, we first make the axes of the bolt and the hole coincide. To do this, we can either select the shaft of the bolt and the inside of the hole, or we can select the head of the bolt and the hole. Since the thread can cause problems with the selection, we decide to select the side face of the head of the bolt and the inside of the hole (CTRL key pressed). It doesn't matter whether we choose the head or the thread because here we are only concerned with the axis of the bolt.

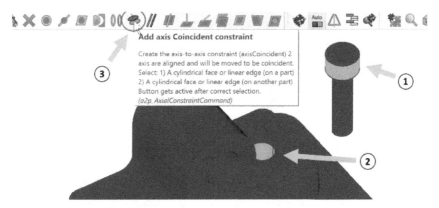

After clicking on "Accept" the bolt will hover over the hole. Now we still have to mount the lower side of the bolt head on the plane of the fastener. For this, we select the constraint "Add planeCoincident constraint".

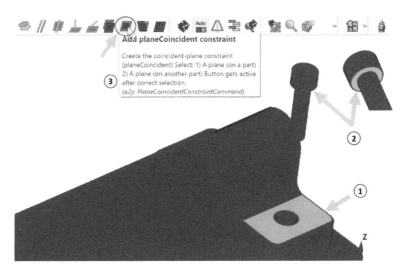

By the way, we could have linked the bolt head first and then the axes. But then we would have had a hard time selecting the two axes. You are welcome to try this out. So, it makes sense to think in advance about the easiest way to link them.

Now the bolt is completely placed. We no longer need to link it to the mounting plate, as the fastening part is already firmly linked to it. The links therefore build on each other and are interdependent.

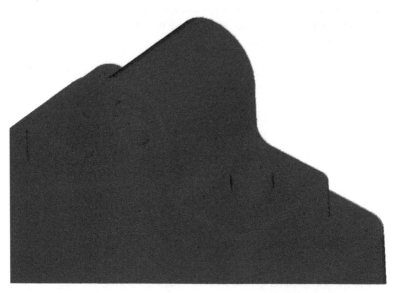

We need one more bolt, which we link to the opposite hole in an identical way. Since there is already a bolt in our assembly, we can simply duplicate it as an alternative to reinserting it. We do this by selecting the desired single part in the part browser and clicking on the "Create duplicate of a part" command. It takes a few seconds, and we get another bolt that we can then place.

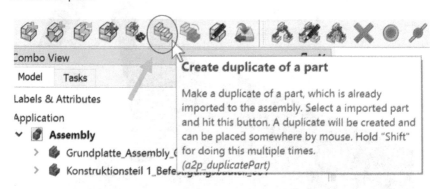

Create duplicate of a part

Make a duplicate of a part, which is already imported to the assembly. Select a imported part and hit this button. A duplicate will be created and can be placed somewhere by mouse. Hold "Shift" for doing this multiple times.
(a2p_duplicatePart)

Combo View

| Model | Tasks |

Labels & Attributes

Application

∨ 🗃 **Assembly**

   > 🗃 Grundplatte_Assembly_(

   > 🗃 Konstruktionsteil 1_Befe...

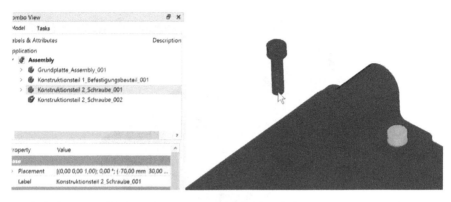

We link the second bolt in the same way as the first bolt, and then we get the ready assembled fastener.

On the other side of the mounting plate, we need to do this procedure again. We first duplicate and link the mounting part.

Then we duplicate and link two more bolts.

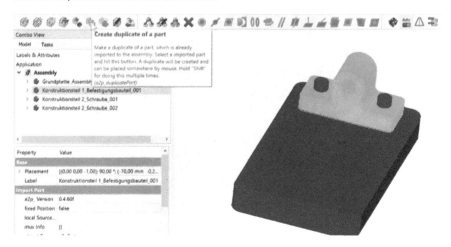

Perfect, now only our shaft is missing, which we would like to mount between the two mounting parts. You are welcome to try this on your own first. The solution for this follows now.

First, we import the shaft and place it anywhere in the workspace with one click. Then we select the cylindrical side surface of the shaft and the inner surface of the axis bore of one of the two mounting parts. Then we click on "Add axis Coincident constraint".

Add axis Coincident constraint

Create the axis-to-axis constraint (axisCoincident) 2 axis are aligned and will be moved to be coincident. Select: 1) A cylindrical face or linear edge (on a part) 2) A cylindrical face or linear edge (on another part) Button gets active after correct selection. *(a2p_AxialConstraintCommand)*

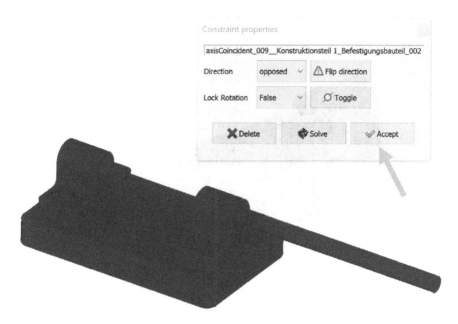

By the way, in this case we only need to link the shaft to one of the two mounting parts, since the axes of the two mounting parts are congruent.

However, we are still missing a constraint that allows us to get the correct horizontal position. To do this, we simply select the circular face of the shaft and the side face of the fastener and click on the command "Add planeCoincident constraint".

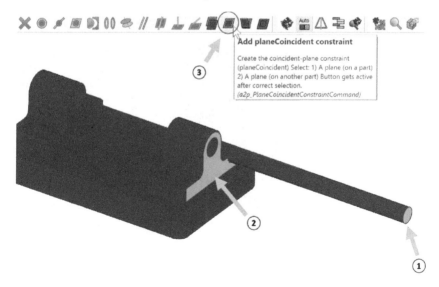

The shaft is now correctly placed, and our assembly is ready. Great, we did a good job!

The two constraints we used in this assembly are probably the two most important types of linkage. However, there are a few more constraints. These are relatively self-explanatory, but we'll take a look at them anyway.

5.1.1 The constraint "centerOfMass"

This constraint is used to join the center of the faces of two parts. To do this, select the first face and then the second face (CTRL key pressed). Then select the command "Add centerOfMass constraint".

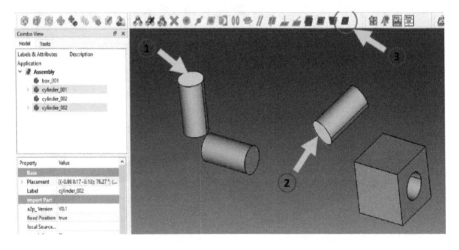

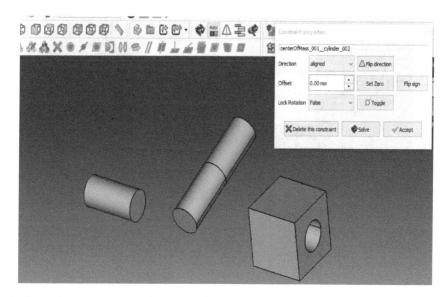

In the settings, you can set a distance at the option "Offset".

5.1.2 The constraint "pointIdentity"

This constraint is used, for example, to connect the centers of two geometries congruently.

Select a geometry of the first part and then a geometry of the second part (CTRL key pressed) and then the command "Add pointIdentity constraint".

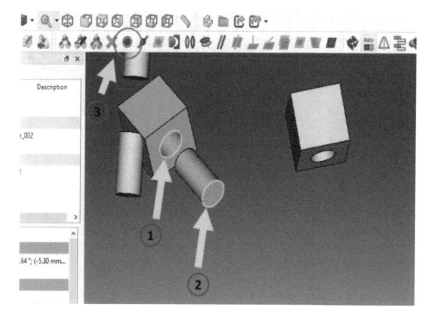

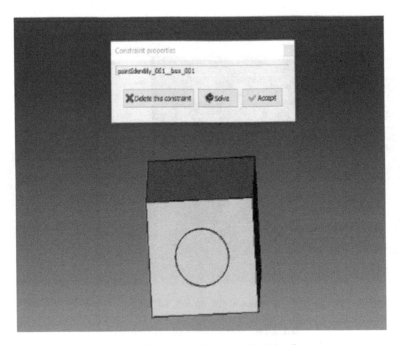

5.1.3 The constraint "circularEdge"

As an alternative to the previous constraint, you can use the command "Add circularEdge constraint" for a similar link.

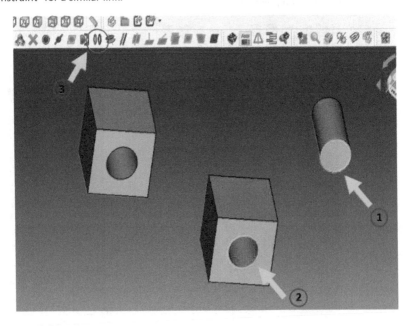

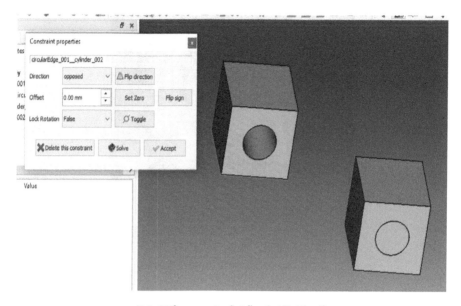

5.1.4 The constraint "pointOnLine"

This constraint is used to connect a point (e.g., : corner) of a part with an edge (line) of another part.

To do this, select the corner of a part and then the edge of another part (CTRL key pressed) and then the command "Add pointOnLine constraint".

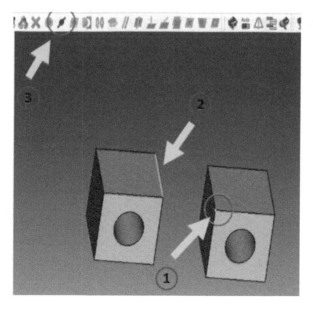

5.1.5 The constraint "angledPlanes"

This constraint is used to set a surface or a plane of a solid in relation to a surface or plane of another solid rotated (with an angle).

Select the first partial surface (reference surface) and then the second (rotated) surface by holding down the CTRL key. Then select the command "Add angledPlanes constraint" and define the desired rotation angle in the settings.

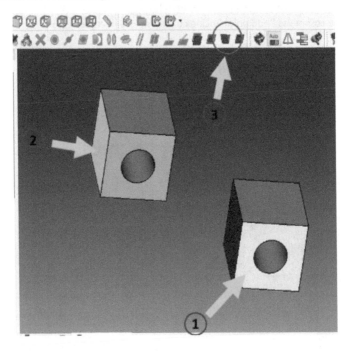

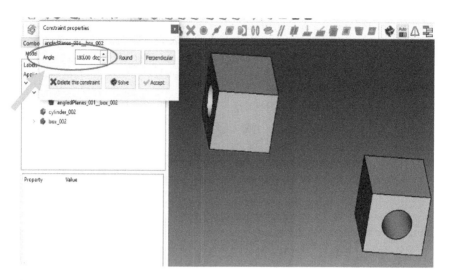

Perfect! These were the most important constraints in the workspace "A2plus". Feel free to explore the rest of the constraints or link more components together. We now come to the last chapter of the beginner's course. In the following, we will deal with the workspace "TechDraw", which we need for the creation of technical drawings.

5.2 The "TechDraw" Workspace

Welcome back to the last chapter of this course! As already mentioned in one of the previous chapters, in "FreeCAD" we can also create a technical drawing so that we can have the component manufactured by a company. We'll take a look at this using the fastener component as an example.

To create an engineering drawing, we first open the mounting component and then switch to the "Techdraw" workspace.

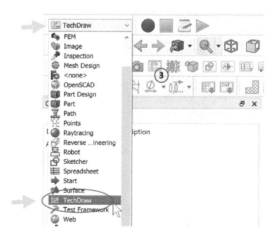

Now we need to create a drawing sheet, on which we will then display and dimension our component in a 2D drawing from different perspectives. For this, we click on the command "Insert Default Page" to insert a default drawing page. Alternatively, we could select a template with the command "Insert Page using Template".

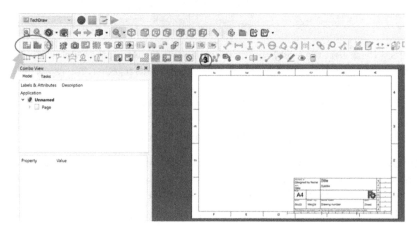

Then we get a drawing sheet with a title block (area at the bottom right). Here we can add the title of the drawing, the drawing number, the designer and other data. We can edit the fields by clicking on the green marker in each case.

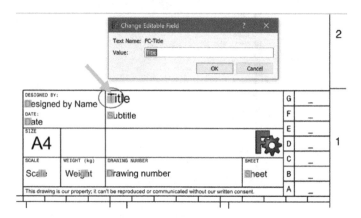

Next, we need to place a view of our part on the drawing page. We do this by first placing the part as we want it on the drawing sheet. For example, we want to get the front view. Then we select the part in the part browser and insert the view by clicking on the command "Insert View".

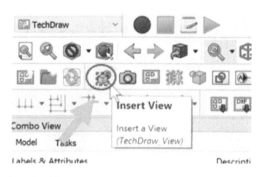

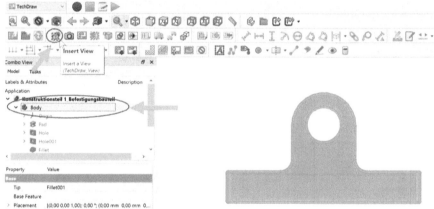

After the click we have to select the drawing sheet again in the part browser, and we see the inserted view of the component. We can now place and dimension it as desired.

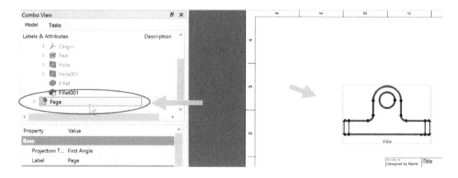

Before we start with the dimensioning, we add some more views. For example, it is useful to add a top view and an isometric view. We do this in an identical way.

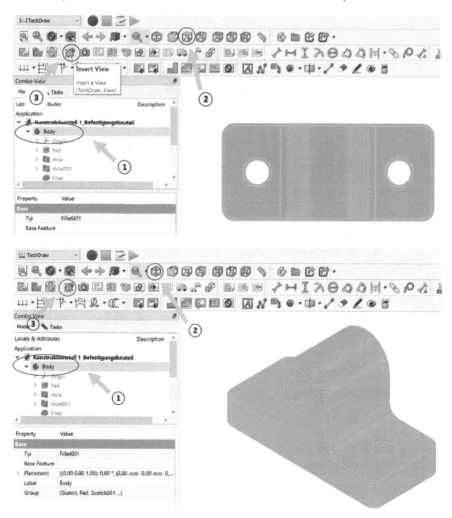

The isometric view is used for a better spatial idea, is <u>not</u> dimensioned and is usually placed at the bottom right above the title block.

The other views are placed according to the projection type. In Europe, the views are usually placed as in the following image and the placement is called "first angle projection". In the US, there is typically a slightly different type of projection in use, which is called "third angle projection". The difference between these two projection types is, that the views "bottom" and "top" are swapped. Likewise, the views of the "left side" and the "right side" are swapped. We will proceed with the "first angle projection" method.

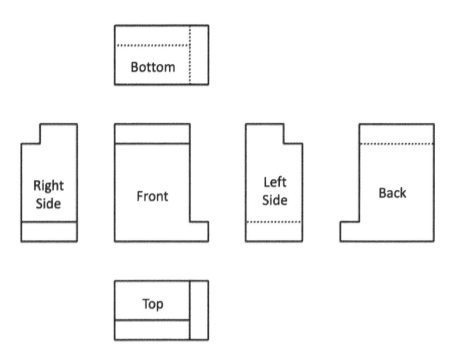

This means the following arrangement of views for our object.

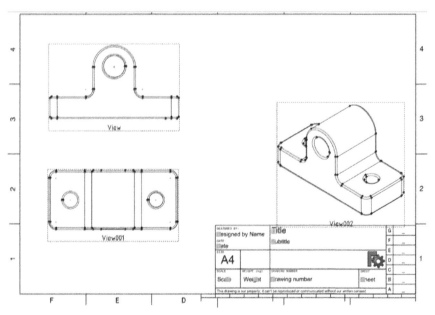

By clicking on the command "Turn view frames On/Off" we can then turn off the display of the view frames.

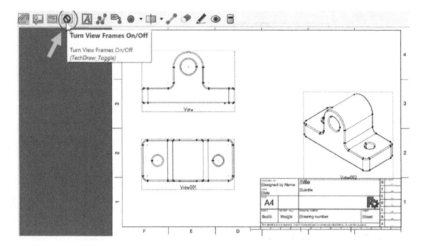

We now have to dimension the views of our component so that all relevant dimensions and information for the production of the component are drawn in exactly once on the drawing sheet. This means that we do not have to dimension all views completely, but we can decide which dimension we want to dimension for which view, so that all the information is visible when we look at the drawing sheet. To do this, we can use the dimensioning tools in the top center area of the toolbar. This works in a similar way to creating a 2D sketch.

We start with the front view of our component. Here we can, for example, create all the height dimensions for the part. To do this, we first click on two lines whose distance we want to dimension (CTRL key pressed) and then select the command "Insert Vertical Dimension".

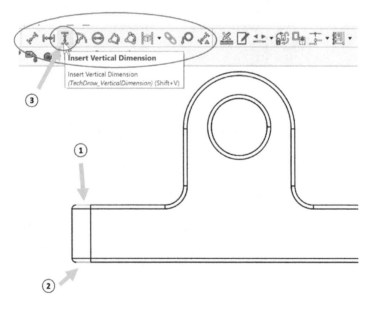

Moreover, in this view, we can dimension the rounding and the hole by using the "Insert Diameter Dimension" command.

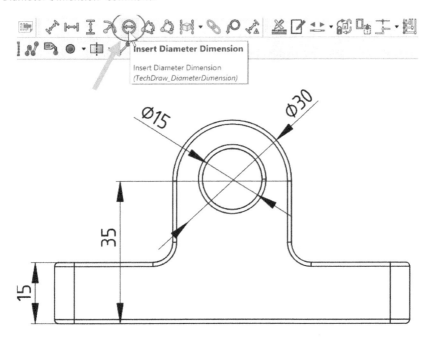

With the command "Insert Radius Dimension" we can additionally dimension the two fillets in the transition area.

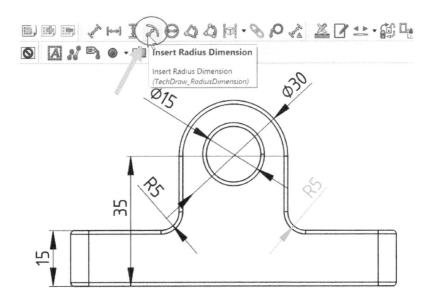

We will dimension the length and width of the component, as well as the diameters of the holes and their distance from each other in plan view, since we have a better view of them here.

In order to correctly dimension the distance between the holes, we need to add centerlines that look like crosshairs. We do this by selecting both holes and choosing the command "Add centerlines" in the toolbar.

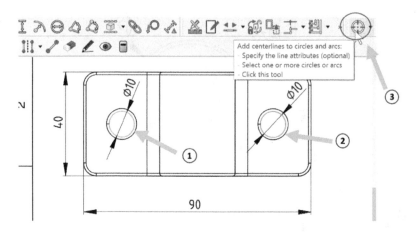

We can also add symmetry lines to this part and save ourselves some dimensioning, since we only ever need to dimension one side of a symmetrical part. Do this by selecting the two outer vertical edges of a view and then clicking on the command "Add Centerline between 2 Lines".

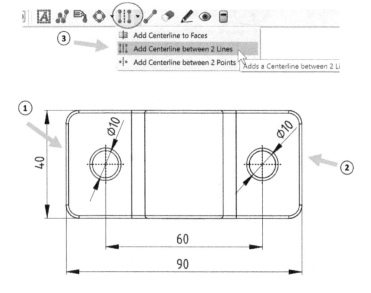

In the settings in the combo view, we can then determine how long this line should be and what style it should have.

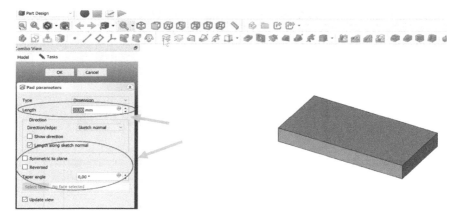

We add such a centerline also in the horizontal one, since the part is symmetrical on both sides in this view. We can thus remove one of the two circle diameters. After we have added a radius for the fillet of the outer edges, this view is completely dimensioned.

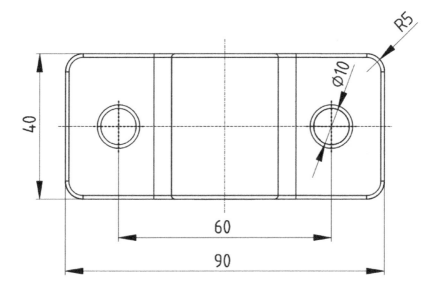

We switch to the front view once again and add a line of symmetry (vertical) and a circle center point here as well.

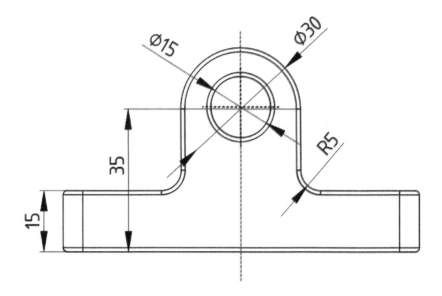

Finally, we add a global annotation that applies to the entire part. We place this annotation in the title block area. We create the annotation with the command "Insert Annotation" and, after activating the command "Turn View Frames On/Off", we can edit the text with a single click and indicate, for example, that all _un_dimensioned edges should be filleted with a radius of 1 mm.

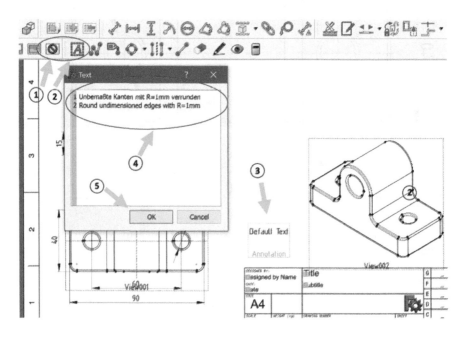

Now all relevant dimensions are included on the drawing or can be calculated using the existing geometry elements and dimensions. This is sufficient for the part to be manufactured.

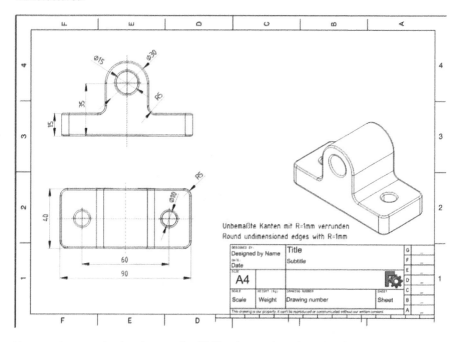

You can also save the drawing as a ".pdf" file. This can be selected in the tab "File".

Very well, that was the most important information from the section "TechDraw" and about technical drawing. If you want additional information on this, it is best to buy a book on technical drawing, as this topic is complex enough for a comprehensive and stand-alone book.

In times of 3D printing and CNC machine manufacturing, technical drawings are becoming less and less essential anyway, and only serve as documentation or reference. For manufacturing with 3D printing or CNC, the 3D models are mostly used directly for production planning.

You need either a file in the format ".stl" or ".step". You can save your model in "FreeCAD" in these formats by clicking on the "Export" option in the "File" tab with the part open and selected.

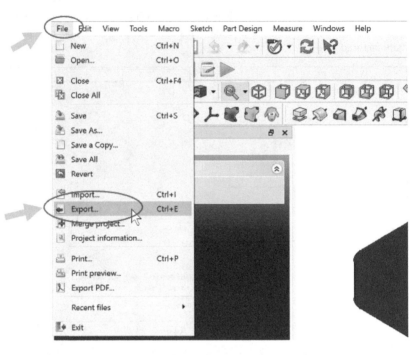

Then you can choose the desired format from a long list in the drop-down menu.

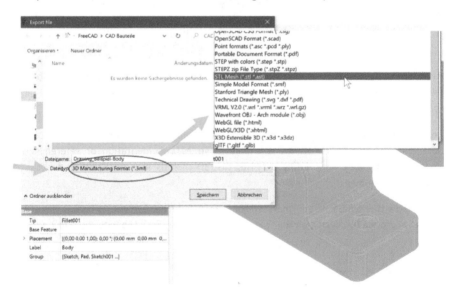

6 Conclusion

Excellent! You did it, with this chapter we finish the beginner course for the CAD software "Freecad"!

Now it is your turn to deepen what you have learned and, above all, to apply it. By now you should have mastered the most important functions of "Freecad" and you can now venture into new projects and CAD designs on your own responsibility! Congratulations!

You have learned all the relevant operations and features in this course. This enables you to design and have your own CAD files manufactured in a quick and easy way. Together we have accomplished quite a bit in this course! Be justifiably proud of yourself if you have made it to this lesson!

If you want to design more objects under my guidance, look for the follow-up book, which is expected to be released soon and will be titled "FreeCAD - Design Projects" or a similar title.

And as mentioned at the end of the course, take a look at 3D printing as well. It's tremendous fun and has great benefits when you can materialize your own designs.

In this way, you can create your own parts independently and have a solution at hand for all kinds of spare parts or other parts that are no longer available but are urgently needed. The best way to do this is to use my already available book: "3D Printing 101". Take a look inside the book online and get your copy!

If you are also interested in another design software, such as "Fusion 360" from Autodesk, then you will also find a book from me on this. You can find an overview of all my books on the following pages. Take a look and get your copies!

If you enjoyed the course, I would be thrilled if you leave me a rating and a short feedback, as well as recommend the book! Thank you very much!

Books on topics you might also like

All books are available online on the usual sales platforms. It's best to just search for the title, or feel free to visit my author page. Some of the books may not be published yet and will be released or found soon. Take a look at the books of your choice and your copy as e-book or paperback!

3D Printing:

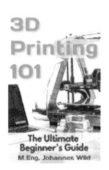

CAD, FEM, CAM (3D Object Creation, Design, Simulation):

Electrical Engineering:

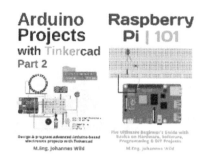

Arduino Projects with Tinkercad Part 2

Design & program advanced Arduino-based electronics projects with Tinkercad

M.Eng. Johannes Wild

Raspberry Pi | 101

The Ultimate Beginner's Guide with Books on Hardware, Software, Programming & DIY Projects

M.Eng. Johannes Wild

Programming and other Software:

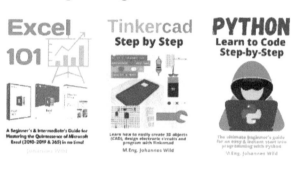

Excel 101

A Beginner's & Intermediate's Guide for Mastering the Quintessence of Microsoft Excel (2010-2019 & 365) in no time!

Johannes Wild

Tinkercad Step by Step

Learn how to easily create 3D objects (CAD), design electronic circuits and program with Tinkercad

M.Eng. Johannes Wild

PYTHON Learn to Code Step-by-Step

The ultimate beginner's guide for an easy & instant start into programming with Python

M.Eng. Johannes Wild

There are also identical video courses for some of these books:

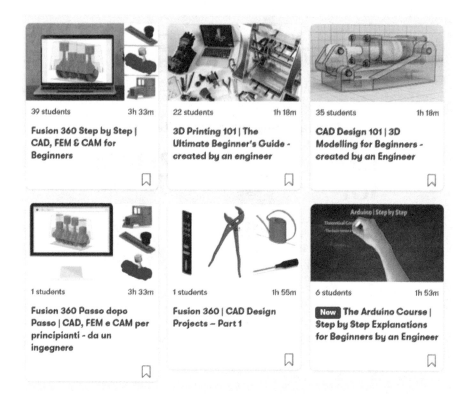

39 students   3h 33m

Fusion 360 Step by Step | CAD, FEM & CAM for Beginners

22 students   1h 18m

3D Printing 101 | The Ultimate Beginner's Guide - created by an engineer

35 students   1h 18m

CAD Design 101 | 3D Modelling for Beginners - created by an Engineer

1 students   3h 33m

Fusion 360 Passo dopo Passo | CAD, FEM e CAM per principianti - da un ingegnere

1 students   1h 55m

Fusion 360 | CAD Design Projects – Part 1

6 students   1h 53m

New The Arduino Course | Step by Step Explanations for Beginners by an Engineer

They are hosted on the learning website: skillshare.com

Be sure to use my following friends & family referral link to get a month of membership for free !

(I will get a little bonus if you choose to stay, so we will be both 😊 Thanks in advance!)

https://www.skillshare.com/r/profile/Johannes-Wild/854541251

It is best to copy the link in your browser to access the free month !

Sign up today and deepen your knowledge!

Imprint of the author / publisher

© 2022

Johannes Wild
c/o RA Matutis
Berliner Straße 57
14467 Potsdam
Germany

Email: 3dtech@gmx.de

This work is protected by copyright

The work, including its parts, is protected by copyright. Any use outside the narrow limits of copyright law without the consent of the author is prohibited. This applies in particular to electronic or other reproduction, translation, distribution and making publicly available. No part of the work may be reproduced, processed or distributed without written permission of the author! All rights reserved.

All information contained in this book has been compiled to the best of our knowledge and has been carefully checked. However, this book is for educational purposes only and does not constitute a recommendation for action. In particular, no warranty or liability is given by the author and publisher for the use or non-use of any information in this book. Trademarks and other rights cited in this book remain the sole property of their respective authors or rights holders.

Thank you so much for choosing this book!

Made in the USA
Las Vegas, NV
22 September 2023

77969397R00089